BECOMING AN ART THERAPIST

BECOMING AN ART THERAPIST

Enabling Growth, Change, and Action for Emerging Students in the Field

By

MAXINE BOROWSKY JUNGE

and

KIM NEWALL

With a Foreword by Ellen Greene Stewart

(With 12 Art Therapist Contributors)

CHARLES C THOMAS • PUBLISHER, LTD.
Springfield • Illinois • U.S.A.

Published and Distributed Throughout the World by

CHARLES C THOMAS • PUBLISHER, LTD.
2600 South First Street
Springfield, Illinois 62704

© 2015 by CHARLES C THOMAS • PUBLISHER, LTD.

ISBN 978-0-398-09073-9 (paper)
ISBN 978-0-398-09074-6 (ebook)

Library of Congress Catalog Card Number: 2015006282

With THOMAS BOOKS *careful attention is given to all details of manufacturing
and design. It is the Publisher's desire to present books that are satisfactory as to their
physical qualities and artistic possibilities and appropriate for their particular use.*
THOMAS BOOKS *will be true to those laws of quality that assure a good name
and good will.*

Printed in the United States of America
MM-R-3

Library of Congress Cataloging-in-Publication Data

Junge, Maxine Borowsky.
Becoming an art therapist : enabling growth, change, and action for
emerging students in the field / by Maxine Borowsky Junge and Kim
Newall ; with a foreword by Ellen Greene Stewart ; (with 12 art therapist contributors).
pages cm
Includes bibliographical references.
ISBN 978-0-398-09073-9 (pbk.) -- ISBN 978-0-398-09074-6 (ebook)
1. Art therapy--Vocational guidance. I. Newall, Kim. II. Title.

RC489.A7J86 2015
616.89'1656--dc23

2015006282

Cover: "Agency" by Kim Newall, acrylics

Be patient toward all that is unsolved in your heart and try to love the questions themselves, like locked rooms and like books that are now written in a very foreign tongue. Do not now seek the answers, which cannot be given you because you would not be able to live them. And the point is, to live everything. Live the questions now. Perhaps you will then gradually, without noticing it, live along some distant day into the answer.

—Rainer Maria Rilke

What is to give light must endure burning.

—Viktor Frankl

FOREWORD

This is it! Finally! This is the book I wish I had when I was enrolled in a graduate art therapy degree program. Here is the clarification, validation, and perspective I couldn't get enough of. I learned a lot from reading this book even from the vantage point of a "grownup" art therapist who has struggled to get licensed, build a career, and gain experience. The path is narrow and winding. As Maxine Borowsky Junge states in the first chapter, "It usually takes a long time past graduation until students feel like true 'grownups' and competent professionals."

The Art Therapy profession is still in its early years, and those of us out in the world working in our profession are grappling with creating an art therapy identity for ourselves and for our profession. That search for identity starts even before we enroll in a graduate art therapy program. *Becoming an Art Therapist* clearly addresses this question of identity as well as those particular to being a student in a relatively new and hybrid profession. It covers issues in supervision and mentorship, contains stories by art therapy students about what they are thinking and feeling, and letters to young art therapists by 12 highly regarded professionals in the field.

In this book, a pioneer art psychotherapist and 45-year veteran in the field, Maxine Borowsky Junge and Kim Newall, her articulate and sensitive student mentee "converse." The reader has the immense advantage hearing from one art therapist who has seen it all and a student who is seeing it for the first time. They dialogue about all that is involved in the path to becoming an art therapist. I remember vividly my own myriad emotional ups and downs. The process doesn't end at graduation, it continues alongside, a shadow growing ever larger at times, but never less complicated.

I met Maxine when I decided to go to Goddard College to study art therapy with her. I was over 40, had a two-year-old daughter, husband, house, and a full-time job. This decision was one of the largest leaps of faith I've ever taken. I had wanted to become an art therapist for a long time, but living in rural upstate New York, there was no school within a two-hour radius that I could apply to. Goddard, with its innovative low residency program, made it possible for me to keep my family and my house intact, but commute to Vermont twice a year for eight days each trip. And may I say eight very intense days.

The minute I stepped onto Goddard's bucolic, old manor farm campus I was sure I had made a colossal mistake. For one thing, I was in a psychology program and I was the only student there to study art therapy exclusively. What's wrong with this picture, I asked myself, alone in my dorm room at night. I hadn't yet met Max.

Meeting her the next day, I was scared to death mostly because her reputation and accomplishments loomed so large in my mind. In no time she put me at ease with her encouragement, warmth, and enthusiasm. I realized quickly and with relief that she was going to stick with me throughout my whole program and more. That she was committed to making sure I had a well-rounded education is an understatement. She saw my hunger to gain the knowledge and understanding of art therapy and she fed it by challenging me and pointing me to the tools that would help me gain that knowledge and competence. She was able to walk a delicate line between nurturing me and encouraging me to be independent, between stating her opinion and encouraging me to form my own.

In between my residencies on campus in Vermont, I was home in upstate New York sitting in front of my computer screen late at night, on weekends, holidays, and any other time I could find to get my student papers done. I felt a strong existential loneliness. I had no one to discuss my ideas with locally, and none of my classmates were studying art therapy to the extent I was. Maxine and I had many wonderful email conversations about issues in the field. But that loneliness we all feel when we are overwhelmed with the hectic schedule of a graduate student who also has a life of her own is unique and unmistakable. *Becoming an Art Therapist* brought all that back to me while helping me realize that lots of other art therapy students go through the same loneliness. This extraordinary book is a collection of conversations and essays that convey the message "You can do this and it's worth it." And we're here, collectively, to help you along.

Becoming an Art Therapist is a much needed contribution to the field of art therapy. Students for many semesters to come will be reassured, validated, and informed. Experienced art therapists will find valuable perspectives on supervision, teaching and mentorship. In *Becoming an Art Therapist* the authors refer to Yalom's book, *The Gift of Therapy*. These authors' gift to art therapy is this well done book.

Ellen Greene Stewart, MA, LCAT, ATR-BC
Art Therapist
Roxbury, New York

Author: *Superheroes Unmasked* and *Kaleidoscope, Color and Form Illuminate Darkness: An Exploration of Art Therapy and Exercises for Dementia*

PREFACE

No one should look here for a "how to" book. This isn't it. This book is about the *experience* of becoming an art therapist. It is about what students think about and feel. Education to become an art therapist should be transformative and life changing. If the student begins art therapy education and graduates the same, only older, the necessary life transformation which can produce a beginning art therapist of quality and knowledge has failed.

Over the years, when I was an art therapy professor, students would come asking for a book to read to supplement their experience of becoming an art therapist. I knew they were looking for echoes of their own "studenthood" in print. Finding a writer who personally described her own fits and starts as a student mirrored my own experience, enabling me to bounce my experience against her story. When I found a good one, it was very moving for me and often some of my best learning. Another's deep story of "becoming" made me feel less alone in my own student angst. I believe a good book can *normalize* elements of the student experience which many students find troubling–often thinking they are unique–and it can make the inherent and necessary on-going ambiguity of becoming an art therapist bearable.

Graduate school to become an art therapy clinician is almost always unlike any other education the student has encountered before. It is not, and should not be, what many have become used to–the transferring of essential information and relevant techniques from faculty to student, sitting in a class to receive information, the student chewing it over and giving it back–usually in the form of papers and presentations. One year, after teaching my first class, I had a crying student in my office saying that at the Ivy League school she had graduated from, she was used to taking notes in an organized outlined fashion. She complained I didn't teach that way (she was right; I didn't), and therefore she would have to leave. I calmed her fears and eventually she got used to the difference and graduated on time as an art therapist.

A good graduate art therapy program offers the student a protected and nurturing environment in which to be supported, encouraged, and offered the rare chance to grow as a human; essential is the student's obligation to

become more self-aware. Along with this, of course, the student in an educational program must gain the necessary beginning skill-set to work with
"real" human beings. Some students come thinking that if they just learn the
"right" art therapy directive or technique, they will be a successful therapist
and all will go well with the client leading to grand breakthroughs and ultimate healing. Current theory overlay in graduate programs of Jungian,
humanist, and behavioral frameworks and how they relate to art therapy can
be even more overwhelming and can add to insecurity and confusion.

Whatever theory orientation is espoused, a good graduate program pro-
claims that the human condition and the art image are mysterious, complex,
and interesting; they are always *both process and content.* A student must be
taught that everything, and all behavior, including her or his own, *has meaning.* Self awareness of the student's behavior and the uses of it in therapy are
important parts of training to be an art therapist. In therapy training, this is
sometimes called "use of self."

The educational program's primary mission is to create an effective "holding environment" that offers support for a student to struggle and grow—and
without which—it is probably all but impossible to learn. Unquestionably,
this holding environment is the cauldron in which "becoming" takes hold.
How safe and supported he or she feels often makes the difference between
whether the student can go on to become an effective practitioner after graduation.

Along the way, necessary information is conveyed. But mere information
isn't the center of this transformative experience, nor its meaning: An art
therapy education is intended, through art, to help the student work with people who are hopeless and despairing, who are suffering and in psychic and
perhaps physical pain. In order to learn how to do it, they must do it—and,
like a medical intern, they must usually do it before they feel ready. One
additional problem may be that many art therapy instructors are fairly new
to the field themselves and have difficulties with self confidence.[1]

While this philosophy of art therapy education may sound rather idealistic considering today's difficult mental health system realities—economic,
managed care, and otherwise, we believe it is still urgently necessary. Carrying out this philosophy should be a primary goal of art therapy education as
the student struggles to become. But it comes as no surprise that many programs miss the mark.

---

1. (KN) I heard a statistic recently that it takes an average of five years for a therapist to feel competent. I suspect the challenge may be higher for art therapists. MBJ: A well-known therapist in Los
Angeles said that it took her seven years until she thought she "knew what she was doing" most of
the time.

Luckily, the "becoming" process of understanding, of learning to puzzle through, make decisions, design useful art interventions, and help a client wrestle with change is loved by many students and is often considered *a calling* rather than a career. This form of education is almost literally about being able to hold a suffering person's heart and soul in one's hands. It is an honor and a burden. Yes, although seldom spoken of, to be an art therapist *is a tangible, immense burden* and should be acknowledged as such. That it is so tough to do it is one reason why a fledgling art therapist needs help for a long time.

Unfortunately today, because of economics, health care demands, numbers constraints, and an overall philosophy which puts making money over doing good as a first goal, the model of an on-going, regular relationship that an internship student must have with a senior therapist (called a "supervisor") to help them along their chosen route, may be spotty at best and in some cases, nonexistent. I don't know who invented this method of training, but it was a genius move because when the student has a good clinical supervisor, the client in treatment has the added benefit of an experienced therapist's brain and heart and the internship student has this expertise and support to take risks as well.

The *supervisor as role model* is intrinsic in this relationship. Not unlike the model for a fledgling doctor, through their teaching, each mental health supervisor contributes to the development of their supervisee, to the larger profession and to the excellent training of the new generations. It was a mentorship before that word was widely used. It makes me worry for the future of the art therapy profession and of individual art therapists, that this form of supervisory internship relationship so seldom fully exists today. Perhaps there are other methods to fill the gaps, but it is too tough to do this work alone and no one should have to.

At my students' urging, I looked for appropriate books in all mental health disciplines. I found a few "primers" which laid out basic, beginning information about what to do in first sessions with an adult or child client. This was sometimes useful and certainly better than nothing. In a few introductory art therapy books, how to become a student was discussed, but any in-depth "experience" of studenthood itself was missing. I found nothing at all on the student experience for art therapists; no surprise. Despite the fact that art therapy graduate training programs have existed in America for almost 40 years, art therapy is considered a "new" profession. When I started in the field, about 1973, there was almost no art therapy literature of any kind, even to use in teaching. In the years since, art therapy literature has been written and published at a fast clip, but the specific qualities and nature of art therapy studenthood still seemed pretty much untouched.

Soon after it was published in 1995, I discovered the book I was looking for despite it not being an art therapy book. Annie G. Rogers' *The Shining Affliction*[2] is an intensely personal memoir of her year as a clinical psychology graduate student. She describes a multilevel story of her experience as a student in her internship where she is a therapist with a young, seriously disturbed child, and with her clinical supervisor—a senior therapist. It also tells Rogers' story as a client herself in therapy and perhaps, most importantly, as a growing and struggling human being. During her internship, Rogers has a psychotic break, so the memoir is partially about the stresses of being a student as Rogers, with the help of a talented and sensitive therapist, puts herself back together to be a functioning person again, able to offer treatment again to her clients. An additional delight of the book is that Rogers understands the value of art and describes and creates it herself—watercolors and poetry. *A Shining Affliction* was a compelling read—the kind the reader cannot put down. I immediately made it required reading and part of my reading list for classes. I felt that Rogers' book was a special gift to my students. My co-author writes:

> [Reading] Rogers' book was truly an inspiration for me to set out on a similar journey to document my internship through a written log [Chapter IV]. She designed her internship to include a half hour after every session to write her impressions. Had I had the discipline to do this rather than succumb to the expectation in my internship setting to see clients back to back, I might have been able to write in more depth and with greater insight.

Our book then is the book about *art therapy* studenthood I looked for all those years ago. It is written by me—an art therapist of over 40 years—and Kim Newall, a graduate student in the Antioch University-Seattle art therapy program—one of the "new generations." I met and, at her request, mentored Kim for a few years before we began this project, which I believe was stretching and enjoyable for us both. This book is the natural outgrowth of our ongoing discussions. In them, we learned from each other and we have tried to carry on that sense of dialogue and response—our collaborative cocreating—into this book. The reader of this book has the advantage of ideas and responses from both a student art therapist and an art therapist with many years experience. In order to distinguish and visually represent the two different voices, the reader will find much of the text is in two different fonts. It is a journey in two voices.

---

2. Rogers' writes: "The oldest meanings of the word affliction include a vision or spiritual sight that follows upon a time of darkness and torment."

Originally titled *Speaking to the New Generations,* Kim and I have written and compiled a book about becoming an art therapist that is intended to be for and about art therapy students aiming for a career. Chapter I, Introduction, is about students as a secret society and the importance of student colleagues. Chapter II is a short history of art therapy education and Chapter III "A Good Book Is a Mentor" is a review of some literature potentially useful to art therapy students. Chapter IV is Kim's journal with imagery of her internship experience as a third-year graduate student in a community clinic. The time period of Kim's internship is September 2013 to September 2014. For Chapter V, we asked art therapy graduate students in various geographical sections of the United States to describe their worst and best student experiences and their most important role models. "Art Therapy Student Stories: What We Are Thinking and What We Are Feeling" contains these reflections. Chapter VI is about mentoring–what it is and why an art therapist should have a mentor. Chapter VII is "Letters to a Young Art Therapist." Suggested by art therapy graduate student, Brenda Maltz, the title of this section is based on the great poet Rainer Maria Rilke's 1929 classic *Letters to a Young Poet* in which he wrote letters of advice and support to a 19-year-old. Obviously, the word "young" in this book is not a chronological definition, as many art therapy graduate students are not "young." They come to their educations at all ages and often with a good deal of useful life experience. Rather, "young" here means "new." It signifies being *new* to the profession of art therapy. In Chapter VII, 12 senior art therapists, each with many years of experience in the field, write a personal letter to the coming generations of art therapists. The letter writers are all pioneers in the art therapy field. They express hopes, dreams, admonitions, and fears for the individual art therapy clinician and sometimes for the profession. Many write about their visions for the future. The art therapist/writers chosen for this book were invited to contribute a letter primarily because students wanted to hear from them. Chapter VIII, "Selected Art Therapy Bibliography," contains art therapy literature by the writer/contributors along with other basic recommended basic texts for the student.

While educational programs obviously differ in many ways, we believe this story of becoming reflects a universal journey of students entering a graduate program and going about the process of becoming a therapist. Thus we hope this story will be of interest to art therapy graduate students, but also to students in other mental health professions. It will interest those who teach them and those who work with them, because it tells the intimate day-to-day story of the student journey and is also a tale in two voices in dialogue–a senior art therapist and a graduate art therapy student–as they walk the path together toward becoming.

In a previous book of mine, *The Modern History of Art Therapy in the United States,* in the last paragraph of the Preface, in a cautionary mood, I wrote about the development, perhaps the *over*development, of art therapy. Clearly relevant today and for the future, I repeat it here:

> . . . Art therapy is well past its beginnings; it has become a legitimate mental health discipline. But in its very legitimacy, problems may flourish and creativity dim. I believe the new generations must reclaim the courage, force and vision of the early pioneers to push art therapy forward—now more than ever.

MAXINE BOROWSKY JUNGE

ACKNOWLEDGMENTS

A long time ago when I began to teach, with virtually nothing in the way of art therapy books, we who taught needed to do a lot of "adapting" from literature in other disciplines. Over the years, Michael Thomas, of Charles C Thomas, Publisher, has made a major contribution to creating a published literature for the fledgling field of art therapy. By helping art therapists say what it is they do, how they do it, and how they think about it, Thomas has enhanced art therapy's credibility and given it "legs." Thomas' support has allowed the field to become visible in a very important way. We gratefully acknowledge Michael Thomas, of Charles C Thomas, Publisher's tremendous contribution to the development of the field and to the "becoming" of art therapy.

Michael Thomas and Charles C Thomas Publisher have been publishing books by art therapist authors for decades now. While there are a few other publishers of art therapy literature, over time, Thomas has been the consistent one and in sheer numbers, outdoes the rest. For example, in the "Selected Art Therapy Bibliography" section of this book which includes literature by major art therapy authors who wrote "Letters to a Young Art Therapist" for this book, Thomas is the publisher for about a third. I have been lucky to have Thomas publish all but two of my books. This has been a perfect collaboration for me: Michael has been always helpful without being intrusive, and I thank him for his unwavering support and friendship.

Kim Newall, my student cowriter, contributed greatly to our dual dialog in the book while she was doing an internship, thesis, and finishing up her studies to graduate from Antioch University in Seattle. She handled what must have been immense and stressful pressure with grace. Her internship journal (Chapter IV) is a generous contribution to students now and to come. In Kim's thoughts, vulnerabilities, and queries along the way, students will find a vivid reflection of their own journeys.

We want to thank Ellen Greene Stewart, a student of Max's at Goddard College who wrote the Foreword for this book. After Max finished at Loyola Marymount University in Los Angeles, she taught at Goddard College in

Vermont for a few years. She says, "I had admired Goddard's progressive philosophy of education since my twenties and appreciated their style of faculty/student mentorship." Ellen was her student there. Their work together enabled Max to construct an art therapy program for Ellen that reflected the best there was. "Although we have been friends for many years since, I still tease Ellen for turning her papers in early!"

Brenda Maltz, art therapy student at Antioch, Seattle, suggested the "Letters to a Young Art Therapists" section along with names of specific art therapists she hoped to hear from. We thank the busy art therapists who took the time to write the wonderful letters that appear here; they serve as important touchstones. To hear the advice of "elders" is a great gift to the field and a visible indication of their commitment to the new generations of art therapists and to the flourishing of the profession.

Students from a variety of graduate programs wrote about their experiences (Chapter V, "Art Therapy Student Stories: What We Are Thinking and What We Are Feeling"). We commend them for their passion, commitment to the field, and honesty—sometimes in the face of problems and difficulties. If these are the face of the field's next generations, the future of art therapy looks bright. We are also grateful to the program directors who gave them permission to participate.

Trevor Ollech of Charles C Thomas is the very talented graphic designer who has produced the stunning covers for most of Max's books and for this one. It has been wonderful to find an artist such as Trevor, who is clearly on the same wavelength.

Finally, Max's son Benjamin, Associate Professor of Anthropology at SUNY, as usual, has provided the technical backup that has allowed Max to not look quite the technological ninny she is.

Kim writes: Many people helped me arrive at the completion of this initial phase of becoming an art therapist. My family and friends made sure I had what I needed to succeed in this adventure. Jacy Newall-Daggett, Scott Newall, Gehrig and Lu Loree, Debra Cannon, and Rob Snyder were all there for me throughout, believing in me. Antonia Greene and Sonja Sackman offered me a vision of myself as a therapist until I could craft my own. Thank you all!

I wish to thank Antioch University–Seattle and the Art Therapy Department, especially Beth Donahue, who brings the new art therapy students to meet Maxine Junge; it was this initial meeting with Max that started the fruitful collaboration culminating in this book. I also thank my student cohort for being a safe, supportive community for me; I know we are all "becoming" together.

I am grateful to my internship site clinicians, supervisors, staff, and administration who guided and supported (and continue to do so) my development. I am especially appreciative of my clients who were, and continue to be, the best and most generous teachers of all.

And finally, a big thank-you to Maxine who generously shared her vast knowledge and experience with me over many cups of strong coffee and plates of hummus. Max, your voice appears often in my sessions with clients and your wisdom continues to shape my growth.

CONTENTS

Books by Maxine Borowsky Junge

A History of Art Therapy in the United States
(With Paige Asawa)

Creative Realities, the Search for Meanings

Architects of Art Therapy, Memoirs and Life Stories
(With Harriet Wadeson)

Mourning, Memory and Life Itself, Essays by an Art Therapist

The Modern History of Art Therapy in the United States

Graphic Facilitation and Art Therapy,
Imagery and Metaphor in Organizational Development
(With Michelle Winkel)

Identity and Art Therapy

Becoming an Art Therapist
(With Kim Newall)

BECOMING AN ART THERAPIST

Chapter I

INTRODUCTION

(MBJ) In this book, my student coauthor and I explore the ongoing journey of "studenthood" and the experience of becoming an art therapist. We provide a view of art therapy student life as a "secret society" in this introduction. Kim and I met in her beginning months of graduate school for art therapy. Her student years are now almost complete and by the time this book is published, she will have graduated and will be working in a community clinic as a novice "grown-up" art therapist.

Obviously, this book is written for art therapy students and for potential students; it is also for those who teach them and for all who are fascinated with how one goes about the thrilling and difficult process of becoming a therapist. When a student graduates–we assume having transformed into the proverbial butterfly–but rather than a shedding of all past life, the nature of the student experience requires an *incorporation* of everything they have known and cannot know until, as the poet Rilke says "[they can] . . . live along some distant day into the answer."

(KN) In my late twenties, when I first considered becoming an art therapist, Rilke was an active guide in my life. His poems were a source of constant inspiration for my paintings, prints, and sculpture. Rilke turned away from the pull of his contemporaries to submit to psychoanalysis, because he feared the integrity of his vision would be threatened under the scrutiny of analysis. I, too, was torn at that time between devoting my life to being an artist and exploring a career in art therapy. I was afraid of losing my primary identity as an artist. Instead, I created images that led me to my core and to confronting lost aspects of myself gone missing due to early traumas. But the "distant day" Rilke alludes to finally arrived for me when I entered graduate school to become an art therapist.

Healing and art have always gone hand-in-hand for me; since I was a child, my creative spirit found its companionship in the non-human and in my inner world. Images were and are most intimate to me and the Divine communicates to me through the silent space of making something as I listen deeply for the next instruction. Making art is a communion with something at the same time bigger than self and essentially Self.

I, too, found Rilke early on. But for me his "questions" so far have never been answered. I occasionally managed to find some tentative answers which sustained me—but I knew they were merely tentative. My continuing curiosity has only led me to further questions.

We are different in that you say you believe "Making art is a communion with something at the same time bigger than self and essentially Self." My worldview does not include "something greater" or "Divine." My kind of artist and art therapist balances alone over the abyss to plum her own depths, hoping to find imagery that compels and insight that may help a client.

Before graduation, students in the process of "becoming" are an underground secret society. Entering a graduate art therapy program, they come as individuals wearing a rich variety of different clothes and past experiences. Within are their captured memories, as a sister to truth, but not the same thing. Beginning the student journey, they enter a strange and glimmering world which some have yearned to be part of for years. As they learn the ways of this new landscape, they walk the rocky path of their new and precious chosen profession. But while attempting to master the uneven path at the surface, concurrently something else is going: Coming to know ideas, theories, and ways to do it from their elders, an intricate, intimate, and secret web of interrelationships is being formed. This underground student culture may be suddenly and briefly revealed in the classroom, or in places where students meet together informally. With enough observational skills, those watching may be able to catch a quick glimpse before it subsides again into the dark. Rarely talked about, students know it; faculty know it; university administration know it. Seldom discussed, but familiar to all and widely known, the student secret society remains an open secret.

A secret society . . . I have never thought of it that way. I have often felt all too exposed in my comings and goings. The student world is a subculture of the university scene certainly, and the relationships formed there are the heart and soul of the academic experience. Classroom groupings formed to create presentations and projects, dyads formed to intimately share under the guise of practice theory, throw students into odd pairings and randomly selected groups. They taught me I am able to share deeply with unlikely strangers. Some of these strangest strangers have become my closest friends. The classrooms, the café adjoining the university, the seedy tavern a few blocks away, the all-night diner across the street, all hold memories for me of growing into a new art therapy identity. Part of that growth involved risking disclosure of my own story and tending the stories others shared with me—sometimes shouted over a lukewarm beer.

Student relationships can be nurturing, challenging, competitive, supportive, painful, and sustaining. Bonds forged within the stressful commonalities of a graduate art therapy program can last well past graduation. In fact, this secret student culture may well be the most important experience of an art therapist's graduate education.

I am grateful my program clustered us into a cohort I could sink into, although I struggled to feel like I fit in; each new course felt like being tossed into a petri dish where a unique culture would grow and relationships would reconfigure as new intimacies were forged in the context of coursework. I assume instructors can peer into the organic mass of a particular class of students and witness the unique and predictable developments that evolve in the stressful environment of a ten-week quarter.

Student anxiety levels spike, tears flow, tempers flare, and depression hits as old personal material surfaces. Each of us travels both in a public space of academic requirements and developing professionalism, and also in private worlds that toss old patterns like stinking garbage into our faces. I know we all had to find ways to manage our psychic material while struggling to master massive amounts of new information (a recipe for both distress and excitement). Talking with each other about our shared experience can be the difference between falling into darkness and feeling connected to the world. My program emphasized working through personal history and I think this is crucial in becoming an effective clinician. I see now that these conditions also prepared me to manage the demands of my internship in a community mental health agency.

I recall giving a classmate a ride home after class every week in the early days of my program. Our brief conversations and growing camaraderie grounded me. Though it seemed we were very different, as the years of our art therapy education went on, our similarities became striking; I view myself completely differently as a result of our friendship. As I get ready to graduate and leave the university setting to establish myself in my new professional community, I continue to nurture a handful of student relationships fostered in the moments carved out in breaks between classes and during lunch dates.

Something peculiar sometimes happens as a person enters a graduate program: Despite past experiences, plenty of proven competencies, wisdom and chronological age, they are often asked by the program to shed the accoutrements of their past life to become "children again"–a kind of *"tabla rasa"* so that they may learn the principles and values of their new field from their "olders and betters." (I remember a question on one of my early evaluations: "Is she able to assume the student role?")

Being introverted and older than most of the other students, I found it easier to continue my travels within the already established routines of my life. As I look back, I wonder if, as a student, I could have taken even more risks–I was certainly aware of conserving my efforts in the end.

Faculty are regarded as the keepers of the keys to the kingdom of the art therapy profession. If the student, learns diligently and well enough, at graduation, some keys are given to the student to take away into the world. Faculty are not the only ones who believe in this hierarchical worldview–students believe it, too. Students come and go; they pass through the university and leave, but faculty remain as the continuity and physical manifestation of the institution and of the art therapy profession.

I want to say loudly that I am not proclaiming that students have nothing to learn from faculty and faculty have nothing to teach–far from it. Many students come seeking the *information* about how to do it, in social activist Paulo Friere's term "the banking theory of education" (the person puts in money and takes out information). But information is only a small piece of the nuanced education required to become an art therapist. A student's progression through the dips and slides of the rocky pathway, until they reach the career of art therapist is much more of a *personal collaboration of student and faculty member* than is typically acknowledged or spoken about. I believe this collaboration could be much more closely attended to and managed for the benefit of the student's learning by program, faculty, and students. There is a peculiar irony currently, in the days of distance learning and virtual realities, of midlife professionals becoming students and more people undertaking education as a second act (or even later)–that this hierarchical split and distance usually still prevails. But it does. All too often forgotten is Anna's reminder from Rogers and Hammerstein's *Anna and the King of Siam,* "By your students you'll be taught."

French writer and Nobel Prize winner Andre Gide said: "One doesn't discover new lands without consenting to lose sight of the shore." Undertaking the journey to become an art therapist, the student must loosen the bonds and attachments of previous life, sometimes letting go altogether, to enter an ambiguous land in which there are few designated, familiar, and lasting landmarks. Student relationships offer a touchstone island of stability in this otherwise shifting world.

I recall an intense experience: For research class, a team of us created and implemented a qualitative study. The pressures of the class–learning, designing, and implementing a research project tied to a practicum site (the practicum experience also being brand new for all of us) threw our tight-knit group into major interpersonal angst. In the end, relationships collapsed and we disbanded, exhausted. I felt troubled by the experience. I certainly learned how I (and others) operate under pressure and I came to see how the course design itself created certain conditions of discord. (Other groups suffered similar distress.) In this way, the academic setting sets powerful conditions for both the coming together and the breaking apart of connection. At the end of each quarter, for example, intensely formed communities immediately dissolve; it is completely artificial and authentic simultaneously–very strange. I recently saw one of the members of that research team and the warmth between us surprised me.

Pain is an intrinsic and usually unacknowledged part of the student journey. Rather than being a problem to be avoided, the experience of pain and moving though it, is perhaps the most important learning that the student can encounter in the controlled and supportive environment of graduate school. If one has not suffered, she or he cannot understand suffering and suffering will be a predominant component of any future career as an art therapist. Within this context, pain is a gift. I am reminded of a drug that used to be given during childbirth which supposedly caused the mother to "forget" the pain of labor. As the art therapy student labors to become a professional, essential is the persistent memory of vulnerability and pain and the ability to keep it close, but not allow it to overwhelm. I remember that many of the papers I wrote in graduate school had on them my dried tears.

Experiencing pain, being aware and even creating it, were encouraged in our art therapy program. There was just as much pain available as a student might want to subject her or himself to. Whether deciding to take on the full course load while muscling through jobs and family obligations at the same time, surviving divorces, deaths, and all the ways life happens, it seems every student experienced significant challenges in the march toward graduation. Early in the program, when we were just getting acquainted, required was our family of origin course; for some of us that meant immersing oneself into multiple decades of review, synthesis–and often pain. I was grateful to already have had many years of personal therapy to draw upon and yet the expectation of reviewing unfinished business (the title of the final paper in that course) was just as nauseating for me as it must have been for the students who may have been bumping up against their personal, historical material for the first time. The atmosphere of that class was like a dark thick cloud. In fact, I was prompted to design a ritual to expel the heaviness still lingering in the corners of our classroom. I immediately came to appreciate the ability of art to articulate the convoluted, heavily defended, and often obscured patterns we have all inherited and unknowingly practice. In class, we shared our deepest hurts and saw in each other what we knew we would be witnessing in our future clients. Our cohort was closest then. Eventually, we began to project ourselves into the future with concerns over practicum sites, research projects, required hours, sufficient credits, and the culminating event of internship–defense mechanisms? I still have the work made in that class and consider it some of the most profound in my whole professional career as a fine artist.

Crucial to art therapy education, of course, is the importance of the created image. Contemporary art therapy students often come to graduate education having experienced this for themselves and are propelled toward art therapy by the intrinsic power of art and its ability to heal. But during their graduate years, the student must learn that image making is only the beginning. They must discover the difference between being an artist and being an art therapist and that being a therapist is vastly different from being an art maker. For example, the uses of selfishness and altruism are quite disparate in the two professions Becoming an art therapist means committing to an endeavor–

more calling than profession—that demands very different skills and resources from those of being an artist a necessarily narcissistic, individualistic process leading to an important art product.

I returned to school for the first time in 2004 to earn my Masters in Fine Arts degree (MFA). But after many years as a professional artist, I found myself repelled by the necessary narcissism that had been so central to my art practice. It was as though I could no longer limit my efforts to myself. Although I had been an arts educator for many years, which is quite selfless work overall, I had no interest in education as a course of study. Psychology, however, had always drawn me in, as had the notion of sitting with others as they expressed their deepest concerns. Perhaps a yearning for meaningful human contact finally caught up with introverted me. I no longer wanted to stare into the depths alone, and staring into my depths exclusively seemed to have lost its appeal. Don't get me wrong: I still love the experience of being with my own imagery in a deep, quiet solitude; there is nothing like it and it continually restores me. But somewhere along the way, it stopped being enough. In art therapy the Self is revealed through relationship, and my concern shifted from being an art maker to being an art therapist and to that nonexclusive Self.

Students must learn that the truism which they believe—making art is always healing—is not so; in fact, it can be dangerous. Creating a strong identity as an art therapist can be a tricky business, particularly in dual degree programs where the siren call of other easier, "talking" therapeutic disciplines is ever-present, seductively calling out.

Dual-degree programs add to the art therapy student's insecurity and confusion and create difficulties in developing an art therapist identity. I think of myself as developing into an art psychotherapist rather than a clinician using art as therapy. As such, learning counseling skills has been essential. Of course, I cannot compare my dual degree program with other strictly art therapy programs.

I also wonder if other art therapy programs exist in communities that offer more art therapy jobs. I suspect there is a regional factor operating here. Questions like these were beyond me when I entered my program—it is as though one must be in a program to even know the right questions to ask.

From a pragmatic standpoint, knowing that I can insert myself as a counselor in many diverse settings gives me a greater overall sense of job security than if I thought I would be making my way without professional licensure. Art therapy as a profession is not well established in the Pacific

Northwest and I would rather pioneer my way into traditional venues and establish art therapy as I go than end up in the recreational therapy field, often associated with art therapy.

It is definitely true that my identity as an art therapist required seeking out a mentorship relationship beyond that offered by my university, and at times, I have had to really pressure myself to implement art therapy, to the point of making myself accountable to my mentor. Faced with general ignorance or even outright dismissal about what art therapy is, it would be so easy to lose the art therapy in the midst of the pressures of internship.

Many art therapy programs, being aware of the essential need for art therapists to work in the community upon graduation, beginning about 1989, programs took on additional curriculum from a mental health discipline so that graduates could become eligible for state licensing. Thus the legal basis for practice was created. With the small numbers of art therapists nationally, and the highly politicized nature of obtaining licensing, it is unlikely that the future will hold much specific state licensing for art therapists in the United States. Functionally, however, dual curricula have not proved to be altogether positive for the growth of the art therapy profession, nor for the developing art therapist's identity.

While art therapy and the other mental health curricula have been and can be keenly integrated, usually they are not. The student may find her or himself in a universe of mixed messages and with little actual support for art therapy both in the graduate program and in internship. I have known of faculty trained as art therapists who define themselves as the "other," in this specific case, counseling. A student being taught by someone who has relinquished hold of art therapy to state that one's profession is a counselor, makes an unfitting role model for an art therapist in training.

What can be done? One suggestion: To date, art therapy programs have been largely generic and, in my opinion, have increasingly swayed toward a teaching of art as therapy, which often moves toward art as activity or recreation therapy. For those students interested in learning how to be an art *psychotherapist,* perhaps some specialization would be effective. Could the specific option of learning *Art Psychotherapy* be offered? It would be taught by faculty who identify as art therapists. Internship training would be in art psychotherapy as well and would be supported as such by the program and the clinic staff and supervisors and by interaction between the two along with the student. The internship student would be helped to do art therapy in each treatment session. I would suggest a pilot program to begin.

Learning about qualities and characteristics of art media as structure is essential to the art therapy student. They must discover what specific art medium to employ in certain situations and how to use it to further treatment. They must understand that art making in therapy is *behavior;* it is both *process and content* and they must learn to attend to both.

One of the most useful and profound insights offered me as I struggled to insist that clients engage in art therapy was when it was pointed out that even more than asking clients to make images revealing unconscious sources of their difficulties, I was asking them [through art making] *to learn to take a risk,* to try something new, to move past their usual way of approaching something. In the uses of art therapy, I was offering the client conditions of *change,* and setting the expectation that therapy was not necessarily a place to expect to be *comfortable.* Remaining aware at the "meta-level," remembering that everything has meaning, has been a quantum leap in my development.

Finally, the student must have the courage to use aesthetic empathy, to go past the surface deep into the created image, to understand what is hidden there and they must have the common sense to know that any conclusions or interpretations they make are merely guesses and hypotheses and that they might be quite wrong. And they must learn when to speak and when to keep silent.

I have been pleased to receive from my supervisor a model for how often to speak in a therapy session and what kind of interventions it is possible to make—educational, supportive, or interpretive. I am relieved to have clear guidance in how to use speech and silence. As a novice, I am continually seeking concrete bits of advice. Clarity quells my anxiety. I find myself clinging to the specific suggestions given to me hoping to repel the unknown, the innate mystery of the therapeutic encounter. When a teacher recently said to me "the reality is people don't change much," the pressure to create change subsided. I thought that's what art therapy is about and blamed myself when I didn't see much difference, if any, in my clients.

As a matter of fact, change IS what a therapist aims for. But the supervisor should readily reassure the student that change, if it occurs,

often takes a long time–years, perhaps–and as far as we know, requires a good deal of inherent ego strength. Cases these days assigned
to students in internships tend to be multiproblemed and of long
standing. Therapy with these sorts of people has little to do with
change, but rather with enhancing structure and stability.

**Interns receive too many conflicting instructions mixing into and con-
fusing ethical gray areas and general inexperience. Having the time and
opportunity to explore the nuances of an art therapy session places them
in a larger container, which school and internship consultations and supervision assist with as well. I feel less alone.**

Perhaps the greatest learning to become and be an art therapist is
both a decided pleasure and a weighty obligation: This is *insight*–the
baseline quality of being and becoming *self aware*. During their art
therapy education, the student must come to understand their own
unique biases and assumptions and especially learn how to keep them
out of the work, unless they are necessary for the client. (Helping the
student sift through this material is one thing a good supervisor is for.)

The psychoanalytic term "countertransference" is more broadly
used today than Freud ever intended; Largely it has come to mean *all
feelings that the therapist has toward the client* or due to the therapy session. While it is absolutely normal in these situations to have feelings
(I would certainly question it if the student didn't or said she or he did-
n't), to bring these countertransference feelings into the work is only
appropriate if it is *for the benefit of the client*. This is also true about how
much personal information the therapist should reveal to the client. It
is often the fashion these days for the therapist to reveal a great deal.
Obviously, the old psychoanalytic notion that the therapist should be
a "blank slate" wasn't realistic, but the swing of the pendulum in favor
of revealing all because it makes the therapist "more human" is not
necessarily the way to go either. Who is the revealing for? It should be
for the client, not the therapist.

The job of the clinical supervisor is not to do personal therapy with
a fledgling art therapist's feelings and revelations, but to help them sort
out when it is useful to bring this material into the therapy and, equally as important–when it is not. The primary rule is *will it help the client?*
For example, way back in my internship I saw in treatment a very
macho client with an Italian background who aroused all my feminist
hackles. While I felt like giving him a strong lecture about women's

rights and characteristics–my supervisor helped me determine that this probably wasn't such a good idea and while it might have met *my* needs, it certainly didn't meet *his*. Sometimes a student's countertransference signals an unresolved issue that should be taken to a personal therapist.

I have received great training in examining my values, becoming aware of my cultural biases, and not assuming the dominant worldview is correct or appropriate. Yet training is only the beginning; being required as a clinician to get consultation on "special populations" such as children, people of color, and the LGBTQ community–knowing my own limits–continues my educational development. Beyond that, to expand my community to include people different than I am has been a personal challenge for me. Even my internship working in community mental health has dropped me into the lives of people I would not otherwise meet.

Self-disclosure is a tricky matter. I notice I want to be informal and friendly with my clients and I automatically avoid setting boundaries when clients ask me about my personal life. I am afraid of alienating them, especially in the early stages of therapy. I am still searching for a good response to a direct request for personal information that doesn't sound evasive or authoritarian. I expect I will become more comfortable with my role as expert and know the value of maintaining distance with my clients so as not to get sucked into their stories.

What's wrong with "evasive or authoritarian"? If the student is confident about how to handle these questions, she or he doesn't need to be evasive or authoritarian. The student must be helped to find a way to adequately express boundaries. Particularly in the beginning stages of art therapy, the meaning of the client's questions must be understood and this may vary from client to client as well as what the therapist finds appropriate for him or herself. The general stance these days that personal disclosure is "good" and the "blank slate" is bad is too simplistic. Like everything else in therapy, the art therapist must do everything possible to help the client and this includes decisions about the establishment of boundaries. There is no "one size fits all" in good art therapy. We are not dealing with labels, but with human beings.

In addition, "needing the client to like you" is a real trap. It is the therapist's job to *help* the client and sometimes this has little to do with the therapist being agreeable or "liked." The goal of therapy is to help, *not* for the therapist to be approved of. I once did a workshop for my students called "The Good Girl Workshop." Obviously, this workshop was not just for "girls," but in this culture, women are strongly socialized to be likeable; to overcome this need is a big step toward being an effective therapist.

To enhance self awareness, a great source of a student's learning is his or her own experience *as a psychotherapy client.* In the past, some educational programs *required* psychotherapy of their students, but few do currently, although many "recommend" it. In my opinion, no one should be allowed to become an art therapist without having struggled and experienced being a client him or herself. For a student art therapist, it is useful, if possible, to find a senior art therapist. And remember: As my mother's friend, Florence Cryst said, "you can learn even from drips." In other words, while it is my hope you will find yourself a masterful therapist who can help you learn about yourself and provide you with an important and positive role model, the reality is, you may not. But don't fear: while you learn about yourself, you may also be learning what NOT to do. And that kind of learning is valuable, too.

Although I have maintained consistent contact with my current therapist throughout graduate school, I often think about switching to an art therapist to further my training. I am reluctant to begin again with a new clinician, but lately I have been considering putting a group together as an alternative to working with a new individual therapist. I also feel some reluctance because art therapy in this city is a small community of practitioners and I am likely to be in the same professional circle as my art therapist. This has kept me from taking action on this.

In some geographical areas, to work with an art therapist is not practical because of the closeness of the community. Nevertheless, when this *is* possible, it is more ideal. Beginning personal art therapy should involve an honest discussion of confidentiality, and boundary issues in any case.

I have taught in four American universities and colleges. I have played all the roles—from teacher to role model to authority to mother figure—sometimes all in the same day. I helped create and for many years directed the art therapy program at Loyola Marymount University in Los Angeles. (I always thought a primary role of the Director was to have a large overstuffed chair and a pot of strong tea in their office with the first words to the student being "Ah ah . . .".) I was lucky to have superb training myself, and I worked in good outpatient clinics, on an inpatient county hospital psychiatric ward and in an AIDS medical practice, all in Los Angeles. I had a private practice for 30 years where I learned about creating a business and being my own boss. And I learned about family therapy and family art therapy which had driven me back to school in the first place at age 30.

I have worked with countless students and still do. I enjoy their naïveté, idealism, eagerness, questioning, challenging, and growth. It may sound strange, but I also have a great deal of respect for their pain, their tremendous expectations for themselves and their clients, and their lack of self-confidence, because I know it is these experiences that are perhaps the most essential learnings they will have. It usually takes a long time past graduation until students feel like true "grown ups" and competent professionals. Until then, *they must act as if they do.* They should not have to walk this path alone, for it can be a lonely journey.

For me, acting like an "expert" has involved cultivating a heightened self-awareness without falling into self-consciousness and being overly concerned with my client's approval. Paying attention to how I hold my body, use my voice (which I tend to use too often when I am nervous, which is most of the time), and how I move through space usually has the effect of slowing me down and enabling me to be present. I am especially aware of myself when I am greeting my client in the waiting room then ushering them to my office. Being seen by another person who views me as an authority figure with more perceived power that she, causes me to stiffen at times. I suspect eventually I will wear this role with greater conviction and ease. I do often feel like a fraud, and I wonder what I can possibly offer the people who come through the door with such need. This discomfort alerts me to the separation between us, which is both artificial and essential, it seems, to create a special and rare space that belongs to my clients.

I found art or art found me when I was a very young child. I still have some of my kindergarten paintings that my mother saved in a brown portfolio. Art provided me with expression, sustenance, and a consistent identity. I was lucky: I was born into a family of artists. My younger brother Steve was the rebel. He wanted to be a football player and later became an M.D. (We were probably the only Jewish family that did not yearn to raise a doctor.)

My mother was one of five siblings—four girls and a boy. When her father had to buy stockings for his brood, it was said that he asked "Do I have girls or do I have centipedes?" She was born in Albuquerque, New Mexico and lived in the Southwest—primarily Denver—for the first 10 years of her life.

When he was 12 years old, Sam Levy, my mother's father, a German-Jewish immigrant, came to Santa Fe, New Mexico on a wagon train. Working on the railroad, he learned Morse code. Listening in, he found out how to maneuver the stock market. He married Della, the judge's secretary in the town of Pueblo, Colorado and eventually they returned to the East where he became a car dealer. My mother's brother Bob—I called him the "Subaru Guru" of the East Coast—had a large art collection. When I asked him why he had started collecting, he said, "Because my father told me men didn't have anything to do with art."

My father Marvin and my mother Maxine grew up on the same block in Philadelphia. She had gone to art school in Philadelphia, was a theater costume and set designer and the director of the WPA[3] costume shop for New York City at the age of 21. Both my parents went to Yale Drama School and ran a community theater together in Arden, Delaware. About their marriage, the family story was my mother was working at the Goodman Theater in Chicago and my father as stage manager for playwright Elmer Rice, when my dad called her up one day and asked her if she wanted to get married. She said yes, so they went to Baltimore for a quickie marriage.

My parents were living in New York and working in theater about 1934, when my mother developed a serious sinus infection. These were the times before the reliable and effective treatment of antibiotics and even before any hearing aids. Although she survived, in her twenties she lost most of her hearing. She remained deaf for 20 years until 1957 when the simple "stapes" operation was finally developed which almost entirely restored her hearing. Somewhere in the midst of this, my father sold a script to the movies and, pregnant with me, they came to Los Angeles where I was born. World War II was raging for the first years of my life.

---

3. WPA = Works Progress Administration. Started by US President Franklin Delano Roosevelt during The Great Depression, it gave paid work to American writers, artists, and theater people. It was and remains one of the very few subsidies for the arts and artists in this country. Unfortunately, during the recent economic bust, no such thing was created.

Before the World War II development of transistors, my mother wore a large hearing aid pinned to her bra with a wire leading to a five-pound battery pack tied to her thigh. With the arrival of the transistor, hearing aids became much smaller—like small boxes with no external batteries.

Sign language was nonexistent then; my mother learned lip reading and appeared to carry on a good life, despite what we would now call her "disability." As her child, I saw a model of therapy in my mother in that her ear doctors sent their patients to her, to help them adjust to deafness and to the wearing and using of a hearing aid. I remember them sitting with her in the winged chairs in our living room as she listened attentively. She said she had learned to listen in VA hospitals where during World War II and the Korean War she drew pastel portraits of patients.

My mother continued to make art and in later years told me that it was art that had brought her out of her depression and reconnected her to people through the portrait commissions she did. For years, she taught a painting class in her home studio on Forrester Drive in Los Angeles. While she had opportunities to work in the movie and television business, she never functioned as a professional artist outside her home again—except for the few times a year when she volunteered her services as a portraitist and went with a group of Hollywood people to military base hospitals.

I believe her deafness, depression, and lack of confidence about being in the "hearing" world may have limited her in ways that I can only now suspect. Then, it was what I knew and it didn't seem unusual. In retrospect, I consider her an important role model, relevant to my work as an art therapist.

My dad was a professional writer who also took up painting and became quite proficient at it. He exhibited his work nationally and, in particular, loved watercolor paintings; he created them in the John Marin style. A prized possession are the wonderful watercolor brushes I inherited from my father, with which I have painted some pretty good watercolors myself. My dad also played the viola in amateur quartets. And with my father on viola and my brother on violin, as a teenager, I took up the cello to form a trio. My father said "never be an amateur at anything." Since I loved him and revered his wisdom, it took me a lot of therapy to get over that edict.

I grew up in the Hollywood community in the Blacklist period. During the Cold War and partially as a result of union organizing, including a strike by the Screenwriter's Guild, the "Blacklist" became formal and systematic in 1947. It was an attempt to "root out" communists in the movie industry. Those on the list were barred from work because of their alleged membership in or sympathy with the American Communist Party. In actuality, this was a witch hunt which caught many people in its snare, ruined careers, and caused a prevailing atmosphere of fear and suspicion.

The list created by motion picture studio executives, included such people as Paul Robeson and others from all areas of the industry. The writer fathers of many of the families we were close to and whose children I played with were blacklisted or part of the "Hollywood Ten"[4] which was primarily a group of screenwriters who, in 1947, citing their constitutional rights, refused to testify and "name names" before the House Committee on Un-American Activities. They were convicted of "contempt of Congress" and sentenced to prison for six months to a year. Some left the country or went underground; some ended up writing under pseudonyms,[5] and a few went to jail, but their careers as they knew them were finished. Later, after my father had been dead for many years, I met one of the Blacklisted writers. He had known my dad and told me the following story about him:

> When I was Blacklisted, I didn't know whether to go into movies before the film started or when the house went dark, because I knew if a friend saw me or, God forbid, if I sat anywhere near him, he would fall under suspicion from association with me and might not even be able to work. One night, as I walked down the theater aisle in the dark, I heard your father's voice calling "Hey ____. Come sit next to me!" I never forgot it.

---

4. German writer Bertolt Brecht was originally a part of the group. But he left the country the day after his inquest.

5. Thirteen years later in 1960, Kirk Douglas, who produced and starred in the film, acknowledged that the writer of "Spartacus" was Dalton Trumbo, who had been Blacklisted and was living in Europe. Trumbo had won a 1956 Oscar for the screenplay of "The Brave One" under the pseudonym "Robert Rich." Douglas' bravery was a major event in effectively ending the Blacklist. (The author of the book *Spartacus,* Howard Fast, on which the movie was based, had also been Blacklisted and had to self publish his book.) The House Committee on Un-American Activities thrived for 29 years.

The Screenwriter's Guild, founded in 1921 and affiliated with the Authors' League was essentially a union for the protection of movie writers and their products. It was this organization that worked out the system of film credits for writers still largely in use today. My father was a mover and shaker in the early years of this organization and was an important role model for me in that he believed in justice and bravely supported what he felt was right, often in the face of powerful opposition. I am definitely in the family business.

After a lifetime as a movie writer and a novelist who published a book about King Arthur, my father spent his last years teaching playwriting and screenwriting at UCLA. As a teacher, he had the advantage of knowing the ropes of the practical world of the movie business, but for me, his sense of humor, attention to and affection for his students, and his willingness to spend extra time with them if they needed it, offered me another important role model.

When I was 12, full of adolescent angst and fear, I entered the newly opened Palms Junior High School in Los Angeles, took the Iowa Test and was placed in the "dumb class." (This is called "Tracking.") Of course, they didn't call it the "dumb class," but I knew and they knew. And, probably the students in the class, all strange to me, knew. I was in pain and terribly lonely. My mother took on the school but it did no good—it was the years when parents held little power in schools. I stopped going to school very often and when I did go, I sat in the back of the class endlessly knitting misshapen garments—half listening.

Instead of sending me to a shrink, which some parents might have done, my smart mother enrolled me in an art class which saved my life and changed my life. At 77, it remains a sustaining touchstone and one of the most important events of my lifetime journey. I wrote about this experience in my first book[6]:

> When I was 12 years old, I attended a children's Saturday art class at the Kann Institute of Art in Los Angeles. The teacher, an energetic, gray-haired woman named Eula Long, was interested in the psychological aspects of the creative process and, in particular, was a student of Gestalt psychology which she used to inform her teaching [and she

---

6. Junge, M. (1994). A History of Art Therapy in the United States, Mundelein, Illinois: The American Art Therapy Association.

talked about it all in class!] . . . She believed that a supportive emotional environment was essential to the creation of art–that no child's art should be criticized but only praised, and that the teaching of technique was not only unimportant but hindered or even stopped the child's creativity entirely. She discouraged visual clichés and stereotypes that typically represent a defensiveness against an inner process of exploration and she valued fantasy, imagination and the directness of feeling essential to all true artistic products.

I attended Eula's class until I was fifteen and began "real" art school on Saturdays in addition to my high school work. There, I found that mostly technical skills were taught and the inner spirit of art, the creative process itself was seldom encouraged or nurtured.

. . . [in Eula's class] I watched my drawings and paintings, at first stilted and self-conscious take on a richness and excitement that began to be recognized by parents, teachers and friends [and most importantly, by ME]. My artwork won prizes all over Los Angeles. With Eula, I had the privilege of experiencing the therapeutic power and the possibility intrinsic in art. My life was irrevocably changed and Eula Long, in large measure contributed to my later career as an art therapist (for reference, see Footnote 6).

Sound like art therapy? I have some of those early drawings from Eula's class. They have a sense of life about them that I still relish today.

I love hearing the early experiences that created your path as an art therapist. I like learning more about who you were and are and your unfolding. It is just this kind of rich narrative that draws me and I assume all art therapists into the field. Here are some of mine:

I returned to graduate school in my early fifties in large part to synthesize the parallel interests of my life into a whole, and to return to a calling that sounded earlier in my life. I approached graduate school with a strong belief system and the intention to weave the passions of my life: spirituality, art, and transpersonal psychology into a coherent design centering on a degree (in art therapy and counseling) that I hoped would enable me to live a more sustainable life. I had been working as an artist/educator in the public schools for 20 years and through this work, I knew the power of creativity to humanize and enliven the classroom environment. At the same time, I was maintaining a small energy medicine practice, approaching

mind/body healing from earth-based practices that I learned over many years of training from various shamanic teachers in Peru and the US. Initially, I found these interventions powerful and effective, especially because they employed the elements of water, air, earth and fire, and taught ways to connect to the natural world. I found that most clients needed to ground these healing experiences in their everyday lives.

For myself, a therapist helped me change life patterns through a consistent caring five-year relationship in which I could practice new ways of being. I wanted to be a helper like her, and, in addition, one who engaged creativity to reveal and heal.

As I made my way through the art therapy/counseling program–although assisting the ego to function well is essential–I found I was most drawn to theories opening to something beyond the ego. In the theoretical base I am building for myself, finding balance between mind, body, and spirit is essential.

My conviction that the mind is central in the healing process came from being raised as a Christian Scientist. In that spiritual system, the power of one's beliefs and relationship with the Divine were proven to me when I experienced a miraculous physical healing of an injured arm at age five. Looking closely at my mind inspired in me a fascination with psychology. Because I knew the mind played such a profound role in the possibilities of our lives, I experimented with different states of consciousness through dream work, meditation, and shamanic journeying to explore directly the many expressions of reality.

I made art to give form to my experiences and I discovered that art also revealed hidden material from my early life, demonstrating to me that the language of image seemed most adept at describing the complex nature of the psyche. The wisdom of the image, gesture, song, poem, or whatever form expression takes comes directly and specifically from the client–like medicine they have made for themselves. Being part of this unfolding is both very basic and miraculous.

I actively developed my own symbolic and mythic inner world over the course of my life. My images were close companions as I moved from one home to another throughout my childhood. I was a deeply introverted child and I loved to become absorbed in drawing; I found such peace and spaciousness there! I could always find my home in the creative process, inventing myself anew. This passion was portable and beyond the touch of anyone else. It was always mine and I was real within it.

The images I made grew more important over time as they became a mirror in which I could confirm my existence and compose my own idiosyncratic narrative. I was an artist at my core and this identity carried me through many difficulties. Like a long, continuous dream narrative, my drawings, paintings, sculpture, and prints have provided the context for and evidence of my growth and healing.

I know firsthand from my own experience of recovery from childhood sexual abuse that making images provides the environment for the psyche to expel toxins and facilitate new growth because it has done that for me. Images are living restorative energies that contain the healed state. I know the power of art therapy and I am excited to share it with others.

A bumper sticker has circulated in western Washington State over the last decade, it reads: "Art Saves Lives." It appeared ubiquitously when I was involved in exhibiting and publishing artworks and writing that decried the epidemic of child abuse exposed in the 1990s. Now when it appears synchronistically in my field of vision, I am reminded that art embodies a commitment to life, and art therapy, by its nature, asks us to direct our life force into a true expression, which, like a dream image, moves us toward wholeness.

Chapter II

A SHORT HISTORY OF
ART THERAPY EDUCATION[1]

Developing Interest in Art Therapy

Education about art therapy in the United States began in the early 1950s. Margaret Naumburg, the major art therapy theoretician (and the only one) at the time gave classes and trainings in New York, Philadelphia, Washington, and Cambridge, Massachusetts. Naumburg called her training seminars "The Techniques and Methods of Art Therapy." Along with Naumburg, early art therapists Elinor Ulman and Hanna Kwiatkowska took classes at psychoanalytic institutes and the Washington (DC) School of Psychiatry and, through them, gave other mental health professionals in the classes a look at the intriguing emerging field of art therapy. Interest was high in the innovative new discipline and invariably led to requests for more information. Eventually, Ulman was asked to teach art therapy courses at the Washington School of Psychiatry, herself to psychiatrists, social workers, and nurses (1967–1973). Naumburg claimed that in 1958 "she presented 'the first training program which dealt with the principles and methods of dynamically oriented art therapy' for graduate students in a university setting." Naumburg's program was at New York University (Naumburg, 1966, p. 31). It should be noted that this major proponent of art psychotherapy offered her first courses at NYU in an *art*

---

1. The information for this chapter primarily comes from my two books on the history of art therapy (Junge, M. (1994). *A history of art therapy in the United States.* Mundelein, IL: The American Art Therapy Association, and Junge, M. (2010). *The modern history of art therapy in the United States.* Springfield, IL: Charles C Thomas.

education department, not a psychology department. A footnote in my 1994 *History of Art Therapy in the United States* states:

> In addition to regular lectures on the East Coast, Naumburg taught at New York University, the New School for Social Research, presented at Annual meetings of the American Orthopsychiatric Association, the American Psychological Association, and traveled to such places as California, Hawaii and Texas. . . . (Naumburg, 1966, p. 76)

Art Therapy Emerges in the Midwest

Preceding eastern art therapy events by a number of years was the deep interest in the arts at the Menninger Foundation Clinic in Topeka, Kansas, founded in the early 1920s. This interest included the support and hiring of artists to work with psychiatric patients. First, of course, was the acknowledgement and recognition by the Menninger brothers that the arts had a serious place in healing, were not only "frills" but could provide an important therapeutic approach to patients.

Beginning in 1934, a Kansan and Works Progress Administration (WPA) artist, Mary Huntoon, worked in a variety of roles from "instructor" to "therapist" at Menninger facilities including the Winter Veterans' Administration Hospital. Huntoon called her way of working "dynamically oriented art therapy" and there is a story–perhaps apocryphal–that Naumburg came to give a presentation at Menningers, left in a huff, and later defined her work in print as "dynamically oriented art therapy." Thus Naumburg, not Huntoon, is attributed with naming and founding art therapy as a separate profession.

In 1937, a journal article, "Encouraging Fantasy Expression in Children," was published by two Menninger staff members, Jeanetta Lyle and Ruth Faison Shaw. This paper should be considered a precursor of art therapy in that it used drawings to explore children's inner life. Don Jones who had been a World War II conscientious objector and a local art instructor and pastor was hired at Menningers. Later, he hired Robert Ault; both were instrumental in the founding of the American Art Therapy Association and among its first presidents. In addition, of course, they developed art therapy at Menningers.

The events and people at Menningers were typically omitted from early art therapy histories and those who wrote histories focused on north easterners alone who were attributed with founding the new and intriguing field of art therapy. (Was this politics already?) It was not until my 1994 *History of Art Therapy* was published that the flourishing program at the Menninger Foundation became widely visible as an important force in art therapy's early history. Over the years, many art therapists were trained there and perhaps even more importantly, Menningers promoted a widespread awareness and credibility of the field outside the eastern states of America.

The First American Art Therapy Masters Program

In 1957, at the University of Louisville, a psychiatrist, Roger White, developed an art therapy program intended to be a cooperative venture between psychiatry in the medical school and fine arts. Unfortunately, there was not an art therapist, nor anybody to coordinate it. It graduated two students in 1959 and closed for ten years. However, it remained on the books of the university until 1969, when White hired 25-year-old art therapist Sandra Kagin (now Graves-Alcorn), to reinstitute the program.[2] She states: [The art therapy program's first] "finale" occurred when Margaret Naumburg was brought in to do grand rounds. She so inflamed everyone that the program was dropped (Sandra Graves-Alcorn, personal communication, 2013).

In 1967, while the University of Louisville art therapy program was closed, Myra Levick[3] helped found the Masters program in art therapy at Hahnemann Hospital and Medical College in Philadelphia. She was co-founder with Morris J. Goldman, a psychoanalyst who died suddenly at age 39, a few months after the program began. Paul Jay Fink, M.D. took over for Goldman and remained an important ally and supporter of art therapy until his death in April 2014. Myra Levick calls Hahnemann (now Drexel) "the first art therapy program to matriculate and graduate students" (personal communication, 2014).

---

2. Sandra Graves-Alcorn was hired by the University of Louisville the same day that the American Art Therapy Association was initiated, invited to the campus by Roger White.

3. Levick, with Paul Fink's help, provided the energy to create the American Art Therapy Association, the first professional organization for art therapists, with the intention of forming a credible mental health discipline. I wrote "the profession of art therapy as we know it and graduate education both began with Myra Levick", (Junge, M. 2010. The Modern History of Art Therapy in the United States. Springfield, IL: Charles C Thomas). The "Myra Levick Award for Excellence in Art Therapy" given by senior art therapists and the art therapy community is named in her honor.

Currently, it one of the handful of institutions in the United States to offer a Ph.D. in art therapy.

Soon after the formation of a national professional organization, the American Art Therapy Association in 1969, and sometimes even before, Masters-level graduate education to train art therapy practitioners came into being. There are currently 35 Masters programs nationwide and in Canada "Approved"[4] by the American Art Therapy Association and probably many more which are not "Approved." Four institutions grant undergraduate degrees in art therapy. In 2001 doctoral programs in art therapy began with the Expressive Arts program at Lesley University. Besides Lesley, there are now four Ph.D. doctoral programs and one professional doctorate (focused on practice) in the United States.

Internationally, art therapy education has been in existence for many years in the United Kingdom. The English tradition was for artists to become art therapists. Art therapy in England preceded art therapy in the United States and was in broad use in psychiatric hospitals as a form of activity therapy. A writer on art therapy history in Great Britain, Diana Waller,[5] claims that the term "art therapy" began to be used there as early as 1930. The British Art Therapy Association was founded in 1964, five years before the American Art Therapy Association. Like the United States, art therapy in the United Kingdom originated from psychodynamics and psychoanalysis, but the dominant theory base in England is adherence to a Jungian paradigm.

Art therapy exists and continues to grow across the globe. The essential idea of the arts aligning with mental health as healing has been long accepted and the rise of communication technologies has spread common notions to many countries. In 2009, Bobbi Stoll, the head of the International Networking Group for the American Art Therapy Association said:

> Thirty-three countries have art therapy or arts therapies associations established or in formation . . . [but] amazingly, the same obstacles to furthering the profession are encountered by country after country:

---

4. The American Art Therapy Association (AATA) established curriculum standards and guidelines for art therapy programs in 1973. It grants "Approval" to those Masters programs meeting these standards.
5. Waller, D. (1990). *Becoming a profession.* London, England: Routledge.

Upstart art therapists are, by necessity, pioneers at heart and seem to persevere against all odds as governments, competitors, regulatory bodies, healthcare systems, payers and employers, demand definition, professional standards, ethics and research validating successful out-comes.

(Personal communication, quoted in Junge 2010, see footnote 1 in this chapter.)

Chapter III

A GOOD BOOK IS A MENTOR

Along with their homework and class work of theory and practice, many art therapy graduate students are hungry for stories by senior therapists which reflect the students' experience and help them understand a philosophy about the suffering people they work with. Everybody knows that art therapy education is not merely the learning of directives, activities or techniques but rather a nuanced rendering of a careful, in-depth integration of art and psychology with a large dose of personal, increasing self-awareness. Writings by therapists that provide revealing insights and tips about the mysterious business of becoming a therapist are extraordinarily valuable for a student. They can ease anxiety in many ways: They portray failures and mistakes by notable therapists and show that, in the long-run, these weren't huge career-ending problems; Instead mistakes and even failures can be overcome, moved beyond and, especially, learned from. There are a few—surprisingly few—writings by therapists that fit this bill and some will be reviewed here.

Reading what senior therapists think and say is an important level of learning for the novice and is *a form of mentorship*. A universal journey is at play here; the good therapist/writer will have gone through many of the experiences and uncertainties that the student is undergoing and is looking forward (and dreading?) to encountering in his or her career. If the therapist/writer thinks deeply and cogently about understanding and meanings and can effectively, sensitively, and honestly describe and write them down, the student may find such a book[1] a tremendous gift.

The fledgling art therapist embarking on a career has immeasurable pleasures and terrifying, if intriguing, difficulties to look forward to. For a novice to understand that the therapist/writer *has survived* at least to write a book is genuinely helpful. For a novice to understand that a therapist/writer has grappled with many of the same issues and has come to some conclusions, is, as Isaac Newton said, "standing on the shoulders of giants"[2] and is a way to pass on history and the most essential learnings of the field to the next generations. Sometimes the student finds that the "giants" were not so competent after all–and that is important learning also. An additional, but not unimportant advantage of an art therapy student finding a story which reflects and adds to his or her own, is that it can ease the loneliness many feel of being "the only one."

In this chapter, we review three contemporary books which we both found useful for students to read. There were a few more books of this sort–surprisingly few, I thought–but I felt some of these should be titled *How to Become a Rotten Therapist,* I was so distressed by the content. First come my views and then in another font, the views of my student cowriter are expressed. In a final section called "Kim Newall: A student's recommendations," Kim describes some of her journey through books and highlights Malchiodi's *The Art Therapy Sourcebook* (1998 & 2006) and McNiff's *Fundamentals of Art Therapy* (1988) which she found particularly useful and inspirational for her way of thinking and imagining art therapy.

Useful as the writings in this chapter may be for all students becoming therapists, few *are* by and for *art* therapists; rather they are more generally about becoming a therapist. One book that is by and for art therapists is by Deborah Schroder (2005). A student told me that she had read the Schroder book *before* she entered a graduate pro-

---

1. I understand that for many, the use of the word "book" is outdated. In an era of electronic technology encroachment, many don't read printed books at all. (E.g., I have noticed that the reference lists for articles in the journal *Art Therapy: Journal of the American Art Therapy Association,* as a rule, no longer include books.) As a person from the old days I use the word "book" here. But it should be understood as *all forms* from which the student can "read."

2. According to Wikipedia, the contemporary metaphor concerns "one who discovers by building on previous discoveries" and Isaac Newton said, "If I have seen further, it is by standing on the shoulders of giants," but the original quote was from much earlier (en.Wikipedia.org, retrieved May 2, 2014).

gram as she wanted a way to explore what the field might be like. This reminds, of course, that, during the decision-making process, a smart potential art therapy student searches more broadly about a hoped-for career beyond clinging to what is written on the websites of art therapy graduate programs. Potential students are about to make a serious and life-changing decision which may cost them much in terms of money and time, work, stress, and personal anguish. It is natural that they would look around for material to read from a senior art therapist, in the "before" phase as they go about the process of deciding whether or not to enter graduate school to become an art therapist.

READINGS

Books described and reviewed in this chapter are Annie G. Rogers' *A Shining Affliction,* Irvin Yalom's *The Gift of Therapy,* and Mary Pipher's *Letters to a Young Therapist.* The single art therapy work is called *Little Windows Into Art Therapy* and was written by Deborah Schroder. It is briefly described here, as well. In addition to *Little Windows,* Kim Newall relied upon Malchiodi's *Sourcebook of Art Therapy* and McNiff's *Fundamentals of Art Therapy* and will review them in her section of the chapter.

Rogers' *A Shining Affliction*

Rogers' lovely book is subtitled "A Story of Harm and Healing in Psychotherapy." Perhaps most importantly for a student, it is a description of Rogers' experience as a psychology *student.* Reviewing it, the *Los Angeles Times* termed it "Lyrical, extraordinary . . . Reveals what goes on in the sometimes mysterious encounter between therapist and patient."

For me, this book was courageous and extremely moving–up there with the very best ever. I read it when it was first published in 1995 and assigned it to my students as required reading. I read it again recently, and was pleased to find it still fresh and compelling after all these years. The chapter titles are evocatively simple and mysterious: "The other side of silence," "Silence," "Messenger" "Epilogue" and "Afterword."

The story integrates and overlaps Rogers' internship treatment of a tremendously wounded boy with her own deeply hidden trauma. Finally, her personal traumatic history emerges and causes Rogers to be psychiatrically hospitalized with a breakdown, one symptom of which is that she is unable to speak. With the help of a talented and sensitive therapist and the evolution of time, Rogers is able to transform her story into a healing one and, in turn, is able to heal her young client. In *A Shining Affliction,* Rogers integrates her personal story with her treatment of her patient, her supervision for this case, and her own therapy. Rogers' accurate rendition of the deep psychic connections between clients and therapist and how they can both change and grow is the best one of its kind I have ever read. She writes:

> The psychotherapy relationship is two-sided, whether we acknowledge it is or not. Each person brings to that relationship whatever is unrecognized, unknown, and unapproachable in her or his life, and a wish for truths and wholeness. Since one cannot thrive on memories, [or] on a relationship with projections, what keeps alive–the hope of wholeness–is an interchange of love, longing, frustration, and anger in the vicissitudes of a real relationship . . . In any treatment situation, it is the therapist who is responsible for holding two stories or two plays, together. The work of sustaining a therapeutic relationship demands a two-sided perspective in order to understand both stories. And the deepening of this relationship over time demands honesty and intimacy and sometimes extraordinary courage. (Rogers, 1995, p. 319)

After she completed her doctoral studies, Rogers became an Assistant Professor of Human Development and Psychology at the Harvard Graduate School and worked on a research project with Carol Gilligan who changed the face and practice of psychology through her challenge to moral development theories which to that time were all based on men and generalized to women. In her classic *In a Different Voice,* Gilligan argued convincingly that women develop differently. Annie Rogers is currently Professor of Psychoanalysis and Clinical Psychology and the Dean of Social Sciences at Hampshire College. I highly recommend this book. In fact, I'm thinking of writing Rogers a fan letter.

(KN) Rogers' book is so beautifully written it was both inspiring and intimidating for me to use as a point of departure. Her ability to describe her shifting states of consciousness with such candor and self-disclosure creates a document of profound value as she dismantles the barriers between clinician and client. In her account, she is both, and she has created a powerful example of bridging the two. Her compassion resounds from her hard-won healing.

Rogers' practice of claiming time after each session to digest her sessions with children provided fresh and immediate responses to the work she did. I aspired to this practice but fell prey to the pressure to see as many clients back to back as possible in my internship. Finding the time to review and digest the events in a session for me was one of the most challenging aspects of creating my ongoing internship log.

As an artist, I am familiar with the struggle to value time for reflection; reflection that later becomes the mulch of creation. Rogers knows this territory because she, too, is an artist, and she describes the importance of her paintings in the process of her own healing. She frequently makes reference to poets like Rilke, Mary Oliver, Martin Heidegger, and Virginia Woolf, and to her art classes as sources of her inspiration. Images are central to her healing and I appreciate her descriptions of light, color, and sensation. Later, when she writes again as an experienced clinician, she is still living in the world of the silent image, employing visual directives such as the "river map," as a way to remember ". . . something unsayable" (Rogers, p. 2007). Rogers' sensitivity to the image and the ways the body speaks what words cannot, reminds me of Rilke's beautiful letters to Franz Xavier Kappus, mentioned in the Preface of this book:

> To let each impression, each embryo of a feeling come to completion, entirely in itself, in the dark, in the unsayable, the unconscious, beyond the reach of one's own understanding, and with deep humility and patience to wait for the hour when a new clarity is born: this alone is what it means to live as an artist: in understanding as in creating.

Rogers' gift of her internship account, and her subsequent account titled "The Unsayable: The Hidden Language of Trauma" (2007), offer me the example of a student developing into a seasoned therapist whose work is centered on the powerful image-making of the unconscious.

Yalom's The Gift of Therapy

The *Gift of Therapy* by well-known pioneer Irvin D. Yalom, M.D. is subtitled "An open letter to a new generation of therapists and their patients." First published in 2002, this new edition was published by Harper Perennial in 2009. The book contains 85 short chapters—some only a page long—of "tips for beginner therapists." The chapters are useful and engaging; a few examples are "Avoid Diagnosis (Except for Insurance Companies)," "Let the Patient Matter to You," "Acknowledge Your Errors," and "Empathy: Looking Out the Patient's Window," "Beware the Occupational Hazards," and "Cherish the Occupational Privileges." While he advises drawing from a number of theoretic approaches, Yalom defines himself as an "existential therapist" working, as he says, from an interpersonal and existential frame of reference. He has had a long clinical practice and writes about it in a personal and useful manner. He calls his book a "nuts and bolts collection of favorite interventions . . . long on technique and short on theory" (p. xxi). He cites Rilke's *Letters to a Young Poet* as a model for its "honesty, inclusiveness and generosity of spirit" (p. xix).

Irvin Yalom is a Californian known for his many writings, including novels about therapy. In my days as a student, his *The Theory and Practice of Group Psychotherapy* was the bible for group therapy, and I suspect it is still a major influence today. I found The *Gift of Therapy* to be honest, inclusive, and with a generosity of spirit unusual in much writing for therapists today. Deceptively simple, it reveals a philosophy of therapy that is human, wise—and occasionally witty. It is charming, informative, and meant to be read "in pieces" as needed and not straight through from beginning to end. In many ways, reading this book is like having an informal conversation with a master. We are lucky, indeed, that Yalom has given us this "gift."

(KN) In my group art therapy course, most of us became enamored of Yalom both through the (video) recorded group therapy enactments we watched and also through his fiction, especially *Love's Executioner* (1989). The gift of therapy offers so much knowledge in such short bursts I typically read just a chapter or two in a sitting. His words have a way of coming back to me when I need them.

Pipher's Letters to a Young Therapist

Mary Pipher is a Nebraska-based clinical psychologist who has practiced for 30 years. Her most well-known book, *Reviving Ophelia, Saving the Selves of Adolescent Girls,* was on many best-seller lists and became a movie. Pipher's letters are written in the form of a dialogue between Pipher and her supervisee—"Laura." Although Laura doesn't really write back, in these letters, Pipher offers thoughts about her student's work and her own, revisits her training, expresses evocative ideas about the state of contemporary psychotherapy and describes her profound engagement with the natural environment and the changing seasons, around her. She says:

> Robert Frost wrote: "Education elevates trouble to a higher plane." So does psychotherapy. It is a way of exploring pain and confusion to produce meaning and hope. This book consists of lessons I've learned from the people who have tromped into my office and flopped down on my old couch for conversations . . .
> Along with having sex, sleeping and sharing food, conversation is arguably one of the most basic of all human behaviors. Two or more people tell each other stories. They struggle to laugh and calm down . . . in the end, therapy consists of people talking things over. (pps. xvii & xviii)

(KN) Yalom at times holds the archetype of the heroic therapist for me; Pipher is unassuming in her wisdom, ferocity, and mothering. She offers examples from her own life woven into her encounters with clients. Her advice is common sense: get more exercise and see your friends.

The mentor/writers mentioned in this chapter, with the exception of Rogers, use the receptive student as a device to distill their wisdom and offer their gifts. And we students are hungry for that guidance! However, speaking directly about our own experience, as Rogers does, reveals that blend of self-doubt and overconfidence that typifies the novice therapist; it is a developmental stage, like childhood, that fades with experience. And though I know I am hoping for more comfortable times ahead, I also suspect the raw enthusiasm and bursting passion I feel so often may fade as well.

The stage I am in as a student will only exist this way for a short time before I become "seasoned." I am glad to try and capture some of the fleeting feelings that go with it as a comfort or point of departure for other students. And as a student, it is sustaining to have my experience mirrored back to me, and even more so to have experienced mentors ready on my bookshelf to quell my anxieties and give me faith and good advice.

Schroder's Little Windows into Art Therapy, Small Openings for Beginning Therapists

Kim found McNiff's *Fundamentals of Art Therapy* useful and inspirational and will discuss it later in this chapter. Because I think and work from a more psychodynamic viewpoint as an art psychotherapist, not that of a shamanic art therapist as does Kim, I did not and do not experience McNiff's theories helpful for me, although I believe he is a wonderful writer. (Right here the reader encounters two quite different art therapists' perspectives, not unusual in the field at all.) Opinions following are mine; Kim experienced Schroder's somewhat differently and will say so.

In my opinion, the Schroder book is worse than nothing because, it represents the field of art therapy poorly seeming to say "this is all of it" when it is not. I was sorry that Schroder did not acknowledge the obvious "art as therapy" philosophy on which her work is based. While there can be much discussion and many arguments about the scope of art therapy, it is doubtful that one would argue that art therapy is not a complex and endlessly fascinating endeavor and an innovative and effective avenue for healing. Although the existence of so many different avenues and styles of art therapy practice can be detrimental to achieving and portraying a stable identity for the field–one that can be portrayed to the mental health community and the public at large–the belief system in *Little Windows* is only one approach of many. This book strikes me as a paper probably originally done by a graduate student.

Schroder's book appears to reside in Edith Kramer's "art as therapy" philosophy–an offshoot of arts education. Art therapists of this ilk develop creative art *projects*–and work like activity or recreation therapists. The therapist holding this particular theoretical philosophy believes that it is essential that the art therapist continuously does her own art and that it is the creative process itself that is healing. She has not learned to do psychotherapy and typically uses words sparingly, if at all. (I remember long ago, doing a workshop at an American Art

Therapy Association. Attending my workshop were students who had come from a graduate program with this philosophy. They begged me to teach them *how to talk* in art therapy.) A graduate program within this particular theoretical bent tends to produce something like a psychologically informed art teacher. Many graduate programs today tend to fall into this theoretical category.

(KN) I have given my response to Schroder's book below. I reread it and compared it to Malchiodi's Sourcebook (1998; 2006) and find them to be comparable in approach. I am not comfortable coming down so hard as you are on her book. As you say, few resources are teaching a psychodynamic approach to art therapy and most seem heavy on directives.

KIM NEWALL: A STUDENT'S RECOMMENDATIONS THREE PLACES TO BEGIN

Before entering my graduate program in art therapy, I read a few books to get the feel of the field. The three I read were: *The Art Therapy Sourcebook* (1998; 2006) by Cathy Malchiodi, *Fundamental of Art Therapy* by Shaun McNiff (1988) and *Little Windows Into Art Therapy* (2005) by Deborah Schroder.

Malchiodi's book took me deeply into processes and directives unique to art therapy and invited me to follow the directives and experience of the power of art therapy. I felt comfort and familiarity as I read and engaged in some of the directives because they felt similar to what had evolved in my studio environment over the course of my professional career as an artist.

In contrast, McNiff's book took me deeply into the mystical and psychic depths of art and healing as he claimed the shaman's role in the healing enactments of the image and of art making. I responded to the meaning of the work he described, and to his passion for the image as living soul medicine. While I experienced Malchiodi's text more as a how-to overview of techniques and processes, I experienced McNiff's book as a call to dive into the spiritual dimensions of the image and to experience the power of transformation there. His dialogue process with the images themselves gave me a look into the more psychodynamic possibilities of the image and the therapeutic process.

Schroder's *Little Windows Into Art Therapy* (2005) led me through the life of an art therapist more than the others. Her brief overview of working from beginning to end with a variety of clients, in a variety of settings, using certain directives, showed me what I could experience as a clinician. She touched upon the stages of working with clients: building rapport, going deeper, and finally going through the closure phase. And she gave a sampling of directives that can be used at the different stages. She also mentioned working with reluctant clients, as well as working with individuals and groups. In this way, her book gave me a glimpse into a beginning practice. It had the effect of demystifying a practitioner's world without an overemphasis on either theory or on a plethora of techniques and directives.

Fundamentals of Art Therapy by Shaun McNiff

Sometimes I feel overwhelmed by information and acutely aware of the limits of my knowledge and experience. When I feel overwhelmed, I seek ground in the advice of experienced practitioners. I certainly seek this relief when I pepper my supervisors with questions, though the shear density of their answers often swims around me unassimilated. My lined notepads filled with pithy snippets of advice pile around me, along with the stacks of books marked with post-it notes to lead me to wise, comforting words. I rarely get back to them. My hope and expectation is that somehow the essential wisdom will accumulate in me through the realities of practice.

Shaun McNiff provides some of that ground in his book *Fundamentals of Art Therapy*. He chose the dialogue format as a context for exploring the issues those of us new to the field struggle with. His text, written in 1988, is still fresh for me and addresses topics in his many years of training art therapists, he has come to consider central. Like Rilke and Rogers, the image is of paramount concern for McNiff; he educates me on the care of this third aspect of the art therapy alliance. Perhaps because his book is so thorough no one else has attempted to offer another such guide for beginning art therapists. Yalom and Pipher guide students and new clinicians in the general territory of psychotherapy, but McNiff goes deeply into the healing properties of the image as it works its medicine in both art therapist and client. He writes:

> The creation and emergence of imagery within the realm of visual arts materials is the core of art therapy, but we are distinguished from colleagues in art education and studio art through what we do with the

images, materials and ourselves. Within both dyadic relationships and groups the picture or image becomes another presence in the room. The art therapist engages the same art experience as the art educator and the studio artist but within a healing context where the therapeutic properties of the art come forward. (p. 32)

McNiff's dialogue is with an imagined supervisee, Lisa, who, he says, is a compilation of many encounters with students he has trained over the years. Lisa asks the questions McNiff wants asked, and this conversation articulates the central concerns of my training even beyond what I have formulated so far. It helps me specifically focus on the art image and the important distinctions that make me different from students and new clinicians Yalom and Pipher are advising. As stated above, McNiff identifies the image as our ally in healing and provides ways to engage the mystery of the therapeutic relationship through the wisdom of the art.

McNiff guides his student through three areas: (1) ideas and process (the majority of the text), (2) a case study that demonstrates his process of dialoging with images, and (3) three interviews with other art and expressive arts therapists and their relationship to their own art-making. In his section on ideas and processes, he presents what he considers to be the "*artistic* fundamentals" (p. vi) of art therapy as he has come to practice it. His commitment to the image and the care with which he comes into contact with the mystery of an art product opens my heart to my own tenderness toward what emerges from the marks I and my clients make. His words encourage me to develop what he counsels Lisa to practice: openness and receptiveness (p. 24) to the encounter of the triad: therapist, client, and art. He goes on to explore the multiplicity of personality, identity, dreams, working with theory, and the role of the studio in art therapy, among other topics. My training has been skewed toward the counseling end of the spectrum. I find McNiff's insistence on the return of the artistic environment to be refreshing. I find just managing to insert art-making into rooms designed for two chairs and not much else in my training venues to be challenging as I encourage clients to draw or move or paint. I find myself searching for that dynamic combination of an attractive, well-stocked studio for art making, and the intimate enclosure, physical and psychic, that holds the messages revealed by the work.

I also appreciate McNiff's invitation to meet one "poetic presentation" with another (p. vi) as he suggests to Lisa that psychotherapy is all about sharing stories and he encourages her to see therapy as a dialogue recognizing that all interpretation, for example, is a creative act evolving out of relationship. This fictional encounter is a rich example to those of us just starting out of how McNiff tells the story of one possible approach to art therapy practice. This book is unique to our field and I believe there is no other resource like it.

AFTERWORD

Dear Kim,

While I understand your reverence and affection for McNiff's book, I come from a different orientation and think it is probably useful to articulate it here. First, I am not a Shaman but a twenty-first century art therapist, who grew up in the 1950s and 1960s who has formally been in the art therapy field for about 45 years now.

As you know, our profession emerged from two major theoreticians, Edith Kramer and Margaret Naumburg. *Art AS therapy and the healing power of the creative process* (Kramer) comes from and is akin to psychological art education and Naumburg's *art psychotherapy* from psychotherapy and psychoanalysis. Throughout its history, art therapy professional practice has tended to be an either/or proposition–the focus being *either* on *the art image* with its art as therapy perspective or on *the therapy* aspect of the process, which some portray (wrongly, I think) as ignoring the art in large part or even altogether. Historically, art therapy education programs tended to focus on one viewpoint or another and these battling either/or differences were often passed down through the generations.

To confuse matters further, dual-degree art therapy programs have become ubiquitous. These programs are to enable the graduate to prepare for state licensing but with severe economic constraints of today, focus and art therapy professional identity become still more confused for the student art therapist (Junge, 2014). With increasing external regulation and curriculum requirements, not to mention the demands for internship site staff to see many clients, *time* simply to focus on the magic and mystery of the art image and how to use it can be unfortunately constricted. Art therapy internship experiences in which the student learns how to use art in every session, today often conflicts with a talk therapy approach without art making. This can increase the student's confusion. Within current realities, the *art as therapy* position is more easily taught today in a master's program, while the teaching of *art psychotherapy* can often be confusing or even nonexistent. *Time* is essential in learning to use art imagery. But within a contemporary context, time is an often ignored and underrated quality in the process of learning to become an art therapist. With the economic climate of many current internship sites, all too often, the student is expected to learn by having an overload of clients.

These two poles of art therapy thinking have never been separate for me. My own worldview has always concerned an *integrated vision*. I see no reason why we have to continue our either/or argument. It seems outdated and not useful today, if it ever was–which I doubt. I am *an art psychotherapist* who trained in school and after to be a psychotherapist, but from childhood, loved the visual arts, creativity, and their integration in human endeavors and in psychotherapy. I have continued a professional career as a visual artist along-side of my art therapist career. Although Naumburg's theory focuses less on the art product than Kramer's (for Naumburg, the art made in therapy is a form of *communication* with aesthetic properties and completeness not being important as they are in Kramer's theory), for me, client art making in therapy is a joyous privilege which can afford our deepest learnings.

Being an art *psychotherapist* does not mean that I value image making less, use it less, nor consider it inconsequential in therapy. Rather, I believe that the image is the most unique gift that the art therapist has. In fact, it is what makes our work more effective and magical than any other form of therapy.[3] My thinking is as an art psychotherapist and within that I sometimes make a strategic decision to use *art as therapy* for a particular client or group of clients because I have decided it is the most useful form of treatment specifically for them. I have never understood why art and therapy couldn't and shouldn't be integrated and not distinguished as separate, unequal and competing approaches. In the best art therapists, I believe they are one.

Along with psychodynamic thinking, I have found Erikson's developmental model useful and I am a strong systems thinker which means that I consider all the parts of the system and how they go together to make a whole. For example, if I am working with a child, if his fami-

---

3. As I recall, Dr. Paul Fink called the art image "the x-ray of the soul" (personal communication, Myra Levick, 2014).

ly and school can be aided to be more positive for him, then I have helped.

My belief is that it is the *relationship* in therapy that is healing and it arises not from anything outside, but from the experiential realities of the evolving relationship within the consulting room. In this crucial relationship, the art image is an essential part of the three-point healing potential. I believe the client's natural resistance at the beginning of therapy can be played out and resolved through the art which provides a great advantage over other forms of therapy.

While I can tease out one theoretical concept or another when I do clinical work, functionally they coalesce in me. I respect that I am not talking about "truth" here, but about my particular worldview, which we all carry within us as assumptions about the world.
Max

REFERENCES

Junge, M. (2014). *Identity and art therapy.* Springfield, IL: Charles C Thomas.

Malchiodi, C. (1998; 2006). *The art therapy sourcebook.* New York: MacMillan.

McNiff, S. (1988). *Fundamentals of art therapy.* Springfield, IL: Charles C Thomas.

Pipher, M. (1994; 2005). *Reviving Ophelia: Saving the selves of adolescent girls.* New York: Penquin Group (Riverhead).

Pipher, M. (2003). *Letters to a young therapist.* New York: Basic Books.

Rogers, A. (1995). *A shining affliction.* New York: Penquin Group.

Rogers, A. (2007). *The unsayable: The hidden language of trauma.* New York: Ballentine.

Schroder, D. (2005). *Little windows into art therapy.* London & Philadelphia: Jessica Kingsley.

Yalom, I., & Leszcz, M. (1986). *The theory and practice of group psychotherapy* (3rd ed.). New York: Basic Books.

Yalom, I. (2002). *The gift of therapy.* New York: HarperCollins.

Yalom, I. (2012). *Love's executioner* (2nd ed.). New York: Basic Books.

Chapter IV

STUDENT INTERNSHIP JOURNAL

KIM NEWALL

My theoretical approach is specifically transpersonal. When I am sitting with another person, I am opening to a wisdom that directs the session as collaborator with me and my client. When I feel this occurring, I especially trust the work we are doing. With each client I offer art materials and guidance as I lead them into their own inner landscape populated with symbols waiting to convey a customized medicine.

(MBJ) At midlife, Kim came to her art therapy graduate program with a specific and evolved theoretical approach. This orientation is reflected in her internship journal. But beyond a particular theory base or approaches, it is our expectation that students will find many of their own feelings, issues and questions emerging in this journal. Kim's internship journal covers

September 2013–September 2014.

Beginning

As I prepare to begin my internship, I invite the agency's art therapist to coffee. She is much shorter than I assumed from her webpage photo. Her virtual image prevents me from seeing the "real" her and at first we miss each other. Finally, we notice one another and she sits down with her coffee. She is a graduate of the program I am enrolled in and has estab-

Figure 1. "Anticipation."

lished art therapy at the agency by dedicating a room with shelves filled with supplies and a large check-in canvas for clients to make a preliminary mark at the beginning of their sessions. As I intend to be, she is a licensed

Figure 2. "Entering."

mental health counselor/art therapist. She says she "likes talk therapy," too, and lets the clients decide whether making art is for them. I am new, but I am already aware of the challenge of asserting image making in the therapeutic process. Fortunately, I have an art therapy mentor who insists on client participation in art and offers ways to present art making that normalizes it as a part of the therapy process.

I am in a state of nervous anticipation not knowing what to expect with so many new clients. Before, I had just a single client in the university clinic and only peer practice sessions during school courses. I feel the pressure to assert my budding art therapist identity so as not to fall into the easy way out of avoiding art in the session. As a student in a dual-degree program, I have had the mixed experience of being trained to bring art making into each session, and at the same time being discouraged from adding art to the counseling process. Professors from the mental health side of the Psychology Department have at times been unfamiliar with art therapy and even dismissive of it. The tension of asserting an art therapy approach in new and stressful professional settings can tip me into an avoidance of added stress.

I am grateful she has established art therapy as a department within the agency. I am aware I want her mentorship in designing directives and her feedback on the results of my interventions. I want her to like me and even now I am aware I want to be part of establishing art therapy at this site. She seems excited to collaborate yet I sense a fatigue in her.

After our talk, I feel more grounded in what to expect. I know I will have an ally and that I am stepping into an art therapy world she has created and maintained–a tradition I want to invest in. I am filled with specific directives matched to various theoretical approaches and populations, along with "book knowledge." Now I finally move into internship to apply what I have learned, having no idea what that will look like as I take on counseling children, teens, adults, couples, families, and groups in an outpatient setting.

But the art therapist and I barely pass on the one day we are both at the agency. I attempt to grab her after the staff/intern consult meeting each week to get ideas for clients. I can see I may not have the connection I am hoping for and I am disappointed. Last week, we managed to have lunch during an agency training. I realize I want more collaboration with her, more ideas, more camaraderie, but I am left to find my way alone–mainly through case consult class at school and with Maxine in our monthly mentorship meetings. My agency supervisor says outright that he finds art therapy to be "silly; why not just make art?" he asks. He was a professional artist as I am, but unlike me, has never set out to explicitly incorporate the arts into his practice. I want to take the challenge to embody the power of art and healing through my work with clients, but at this moment I feel dismissed as I do at times in school. I am in need of overt encouragement, excitement about the possibilities, and examples around me of art with clients. Will I find that here?

Between a heavy caseload and the overwhelming paperwork demands, I am beginning to see that the challenge of just keeping up excludes a depth of reflection I was hoping to have. Reading Annie Rogers'[1] account of her internship experience primed me to expect to have the space to reflect on each encounter as she did. Instead, I calculate my hours to complete my internship within the year working three days a week. This means maintaining 12–15 weekly appointments and staying late to complete case notes and treatment plans as well as fitting in collateral contact hours with teachers, school counselors, parents, social service agencies, etc.

Only over the weekend do I have time to reflect on the images and words my clients share. At home, I create small images of our sessions on index cards with notes so I can embed their stories into my psychic field for retrieval later. My supervisor advises me to "leave" the clients at the clinic, and another intern suggests I consciously leave my caseload behind me as I commute home. I feel caught between the need for distance and self-care and the sense that without time to reflect, I may miss the deeper messages contained in my client's words and images. "We are not detectives!" my supervisor insists, yet the signifiers, as Annie Rogers calls them, peering out from my client's images, could reveal clues and inspire interventions lost without the time to investigate. I believe we are detectives.

I seem to have no choice about thinking about this case. Could it be I have already thrown everything out the window I thought I knew about boundaries? The man says he is not long for this world, that if he doesn't get a break soon he'll "pull the plug" (I have a suicidal client in one of my first cases!). I carry the clinic handbook that is supposed to tell me what to do around with me in the three ring binder which has come to look as disorganized as I feel. I need to put section dividers in it, but that requires a moment of calm reflection I have yet to grab hold of. The section on suicidality has two parts: the protocol and the mini-assessment questions. My client has his own timeline for checking out but, to my relief, apparently it is a few weeks away. He misses his appointments and rarely picks up his phone when I call. Last night, however, he left a long message in despair over his bad luck and worthless life. I reached him the next day and set a

---

1. Rogers' *The Shining Affliction.*

time to talk on the phone, but he didn't answer. Maxine urged me to get a second phone line for clients and now I clearly see the benefit of it. To see my client's initials appear on the screen captures me, makes me anxious, and the decision to call and when to call, all consume my attention.

My agency supervisor goes on to give me information about the many years my client has come to the agency. "He isn't who he wants to be" my supervisor says simply, as though that explains anything. And I know how he feels. So does my supervisor. We both aspired to be known visual artists; in fact, we filled our last consult hour together sharing the heartbreak of shriveled dreams even in the midst (for me) of new art therapy dreams under construction.

My client says he is contemplating suicide, not today, but soon. He reports he has had no food, no money, car, or heat. Art making seems far away.

Am I becoming a small town counselor without boundaries? The line between friend and professional seems slim at best and is always tricky, as my supervisor suggests picking my client up and taking him for coffee. In the span of one short day I have gone from the conviction a therapist should never meet in a public place outside of the bounds of the preset therapeutic hour to considering driving to my client's house to rescue him. Instead of dismounting from my big white horse, wearing my suit of shining armor, I am galloping faster to save the day. I had no idea my rescuer archetype was quite this prevalent. I am humbled and worry how the clinic staff sees me. I imagine them rolling their eyes and deeply sighing; do I bring this on myself? I am an intern, everything is a new experience, and I naturally fear the worst. The responsibility of it is intimidating.

My second client is tucked into the corner in the waiting area as a flurry of sign-ins postpones my greeting. I pause and wait for the crowd to clear out. I study her a moment before she notices me; I feel myself wanting to control her first impression of me. I feel the strong desire to launch our relationship with sincerity and usher her into the safe sanctuary of the art therapy office. I like her immediately. She is in her fifties, a woman near my age, a professional, braving a community clinic in search of a promise of relief of some sort.

On a glass-covered table are markers and drawing paper because I am determined to have each client engage in some visual gesture both to learn how this approach works and to achieve my required 350 art therapy contact hours. To this end, I may have been heavy handed–after all, she looks askance at the paper and at my insistence. She reluctantly chooses a pur-

Figure 3. "Finding my way."

ple marker and makes a simple line traveling first one direction and then, with a sudden U-turn, doubling back on itself, covering a similar distance, and finishing with a turn toward the top of the page; a short, determined advance upward, as if reaching for air. The risk is worth it as I venture a brief interpretation: "I see a sharp turn," to which she replies, "I feel like I am doubling back on myself."

From this modest line she begins to describe her life, its twists and failures, as she describes them, and her determined efforts to build a solid framework from her chaotic and violent childhood. She feels robbed of her life's possibilities; her twenties were spent barely surviving familial fallout. Now, at midlife, she says she is looking for an existential reckoning, meaning making. The same determination that served her survival has brought her here, so that this essential soul work, in danger of being ground under foot by the pressures of life and habits of anxiety, can be received. I may get to walk with this woman. I notice the similarities between us. We both see our own vulnerability and we imagine, still, the places that call us to engage. Now, instead of the expanding possibilities of youth, we are faced with compromises that ask: "what is still possible within a diminishing future? What is worth the effort?"

She says she grew up quickly, becoming a mother surrogate to her sister and a caregiver to her depressed mother. My client's determination enabled her to succeed academically, giving her a way to establish herself as an adult and to separate from her parents. She struggled to remain alive and now she wants to be free of her "old demons" and wonders what is possible. I do, too.

Our second session is chaotic. The room I thought I had reserved is already occupied by a staff member and I must shuffle my client into my supervisor's room who kindly vacates on short notice. When will I master this schedule program? I am discombobulated and my client looks impatient. The art therapy directive I designed is abandoned for the moment as I struggle to collect myself and work to get present and grounded. I am distracted by my embarrassment at being seen by her as disorganized. She is a professional herself and I am finding I am more intimidated by higher functioning clients who I imagine are likely to have greater expectations of me. Class issues are alive and well in me.

She states her ambivalence about therapy and my intimidation grows. In an effort to sell myself and the process, I remind her of her stated desire to make meaning of her current life and address the stress and depression that have dogged her most of her life. She agrees to continue and we struggle to come up with a time to meet that will work around her family, work, and recreation schedule. This woman has been trying to commit to a therapy slot for six months! We find a time two weeks hence and she energetically disappears from my therapy room and my psyche.

For session three, she arrives complaining about the trials of getting to the agency, coordinating with husband, and bus schedules. Once again her ambivalence fills the room and I am reminded of what a therapist friend said to me the previous night as she lamented the effort it took to keep clients committed to the therapeutic process and her refusal to continue to work that hard. I sat back and decided to let go and see what the client brought forward.

She brings her fear of snakes and, in my imagination, they began to encircle the room. This woman has brought her core dream of terror into our art therapy room as she decides once again to stay or leave. I remind myself that although I imagine her healed of this terror, she has to decide. The therapy journey is one she has refused up until now, and I am not in the business of determining the courage and timing of another. Meanwhile the imaginary snake becomes more vivid to me, slithering between us to reveal a slick cold skin that slides through the air. What small, endangered child has need of such a profound protector? I want to reach out to her. But will my client accept my help?

Her face is softening as she considers the journey ahead. Her previous hard-line refusal to allow her executive function to admit to limbic realities softens as well. I suggest a simple statement for her: "I am willing to connect with myself,"–a statement I hope she can craft into her own, held in her mind and heart for no more than three minutes a day. (Any more than that may activate her mind into reaction and I want to move gently under the radar of her ego defenses.) She says clearly "I can do that." She agrees to a regular therapy time she had refused before, but I wonder if she will be able to do this. It is up to her as I make every effort to release my expectations and hopes around her healing. Timing is a mystery not to be pushed.

I read about treatment for specific phobias and discover the high success rate for exposure therapy. I visualize accompanying my client to the reptile house, holding space as my client faces her terror of being alone with her imagined predator snake. I am excited to report to her that, according to the research, she is likely to significantly improve her phobia terror after only a single session of intentional exposure to her feared threat. And yet I wonder still what the snake protects, or who. Synchronistically, I see a large plastic snake peering out from a basket of other plastic toys at my neighborhood Saturday market.

What does art therapy offer? I find I am quick to refer my phobic client to an evidence-based approach that is not art therapy. Why? But I offer my client two circles predrawn on white paper: a check-in and check-out ritual I am hopeful she will agree to. I can see the exercise annoys her and she makes a hasty squiggle across the first mandala, as though traveling quickly across a wavy ground. Later, her exit mandala is a seemingly random spiral, which I note is traveling inward, as she is. Though her internal skeptic is barely willing to let the body's hand make these minimal marks, I think some other self is beginning to send a message that a tentative collaboration is underway.

As she leaves my office, she has agreed to continue her three minutes of homework, which, ever the overachiever, she says follows a 10-minute meditation, and she has added a daily log of times when she is experiencing peace. I suspect she has more moments of peace than she realizes, I hope so, and they may encourage her to challenge the negative spin her critic gives to her days. She tells me she can count 10 breaths consistently in her meditation so I see her mindfulness is stronger than a beginner's; she may be closer to greater peace than she imagines. I hope that a focus on her capabilities can shift the impression she has of her situation as pretty hopeless and unchanging. It is Thanksgiving this week and I am grateful this woman provides such a rich collaboration for me. I so hope our work is fruitful for her.

My client, however, has her own agenda for our next session. She reports her awareness of shame bubbling up through her three minutes of silent communion with herself saying again "I am willing to connect with myself." There is no mention of snakes this week, but instead, chronic shame. She describes a small figure curled in a fetal position tucked into a dark corner of her inner sight. I become curious if she will claim this rejected part as herself. It is enough for now that she can see her. I speak of parts of ourselves and the capacity to step back from a larger Self to observe and eventually orchestrate our many parts. My transpersonal psychosynthesis training has begun to assert itself as an organizing framework for my client's work. She seems familiar with this way of understanding personality and although she has a powerful skeptic within, her desire to improve her life and be free of fear and shame motivates her. Reading Jung reminds me I am in great company. I pore over his mandalas as he recorded his own descent through hell and back.

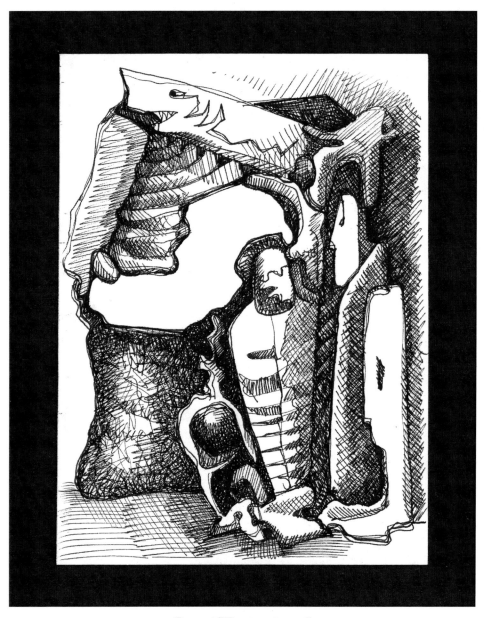

Figure 4."Her story in me."

Autumn

My new client is in her boyfriend's soup of violent pornography; she carries images on her camera as part of the case she says she is building against him. Perhaps she is trying to convince herself she must leave and needs others to insist she leave as well. The first images we work with in art therapy are these vivid scenes of abuse. The extreme toxicity my client moves within seems to already be permeating my own psyche. In a three-part dream I have early into our work together, I see a hellish scene: a man stands over writhing naked women, who offer themselves up for brutal lashings from long slashing whips wielded by this man's assistants. One woman turns her buttocks toward him and a stream of blood squirts high into the air from the back of her thigh, she directs it like a thread, an offering and an invitation for more abuse. This horrible scene repeats itself twice in my dream. The woman in the dream is accustomed to violence. My client has lived with extreme pain and trauma since she was a little girl, and is probably acclimated to it, perhaps even invites it. How can she see and act with clarity in her current situation?

I am in high gear, discussing this client as I consult with my school art therapy case consult group. The concern of my school supervisor reflects vividly on his face as he instructs me to call my site supervisor immediately to clarify that he knows everything I do and ask if I should report my client's abuse. My supervisor advises that I place a call to Adult Protective Services because of my client's mobility impairment. In addition, I am concerned that her possible long-term PTSD[2] symptoms that may be clouding her instincts to escape her abusive situation. Her boyfriend has not physically harmed her yet, but he has threatened her and she locked herself in her room in fear; she is clearly suffering emotional abuse.

Immediately, I try to help. I enlist advice from all my supervisors, connect with the local domestic violence organization, arrange a conversation with an advocate to occur on the phone during our next therapy session, and contact the local housing advocacy group. I do realize I cannot save her, and if my actions cause her situation to escalate, I am not living up to my first duty to act in the best interests of my client. My clinical supervisor advises me by describing the grey nuances of the relationship between the police and the agency, suggesting that I consider whether I want to be known as the lady who calls the police. He explains how engaging various authorities can bring more harm than help to clients and families.

My supervisor may be right and I am introduced to disturbing dilemmas that infiltrate my dreams. I wonder how best to digest these situations to avoid accumulating their effects within me. I choose to see my dreams

---

2. PTSD = Post Traumatic Stress Disorder

as compensatory, as a release of energy rising from a pit of collective horror and dissipating into the love I choose to bring to this situation. I decide to utilize my meditation as a cauldron of light I drop these scenes gently into. I see them as colors, textures, movements, and sounds dissolving as light rises through the images and releases them.

I imagine I operate on many simultaneous levels: I try to coordinate other helpers to address the literal dangers in my client's life to let her know others see and care about her. If she agrees to be in a group of other women like her, she may gain support and clarity about her situation. I allow her story to move into me and then into a vast heart bigger than I am. I let the heart of me do its natural healing work. It may work this way.

My client is reluctant to draw on the paper I have set out for her. She resists the creative process but once engaged creates something she finds remarkable. Some clients retreat from their created images, afraid or overwhelmed by what they see. This awareness gives me even a greater respect for art therapy: for its power to elicit repressed material and to offer a healing response. Within the single image made or through numerous images made over time, images reveal the healing process. The client draws a hunched-over woman with daggers in her back. It is a bleak picture, fitting in with her stories of beatings and accidents in her early years. Perhaps she has become habituated to trauma and this image seems to please her as an accurate self-portrait.

The other supervisor offers to discuss my new client and to "work with me with her." He says "there is a lot in this case." The thick files my client hauls around build a case against her partner's family, as though her word is not enough. She says she is proud of her ability to advocate for herself and others.

I could go on, and this story is likely to go on, as she seems pleased to schedule her next session. My supervisor suggests my client could come in twice a week until the current crisis has passed. She does appear to be in a potentially dangerous situation.

My caseload becomes more intense and I wonder how much I will be able to write on each client. Soon my caseload will grow to 15 or more clients. In this journal, I intend to weave my personal narrative into the unfolding client narrative, threads of supervision, mentorship, and my own therapy as all converge to shape this internship year.

I saw my personal therapist this morning. I was reticent about my appointment today. I knew I needed to take more relational risks with my

Figure 5. "Too much."

therapist, especially now that I am expecting my clients to bring themselves fully to the process, and use the therapeutic relationship as their lab-
oratory of change. I have been using my own therapy to facilitate life skills

and change. My therapist has seen me through one transition after another for the past four years as I worked to align my life with the field of psychology and claim the dream of becoming an art therapist I have carried since my late twenties. Now I am here.

Entering Winter

I arrive on Wednesday and the intake specialist tells me my client is coming in at 1:00 to see him. Apparently, I've been fired as his therapist already. The two voicemails I left went unheard. "Don't take this personally" the intake worker advises, "Sometimes it just feels safer for a client to choose the intake therapist." I wouldn't mind turning this guy over, but my ego is puffing up and I am offended at being presented as a flake, so I ask if I can at least meet with him.

He isn't quite what I expect, this formerly successful man. His clothes are ragged, and he has a service dog, who meanders quietly around the small office, scruffy and subdued. Like another older, life-worn client I see, he carries tattered files with him documenting his many encounters with agencies, lawyers, and other players in his life. He uses his considerable intelligence and creativity to craft a meager subsistence from the thin resources available to him. Interfacing with our agency is part of his tapestry of survival.

I begin to see the thread I am to him and I suspect a connection is growing, although I notice a tight stretched sensation in my mind and a restless, slightly desperate feeling which prompts a growing desire in me to leave the room. I wonder if he engenders this response in others?

I watch as the intake specialist challenges the client's portrayal of himself as a victim, trying to suggest accountability. This seems to inspire a scared silence and a retelling of stories of the harm others have subjected him to; he insists upon his ongoing vulnerability and victimhood. By the end of the session, I discover he is once again my client.

I am feeling manipulated. He is sleeping through his appointments with me. I want to be done with him, I feel foolish. The therapy hours he doesn't arrive I draw my impressions of him, seeking for some intuitive insight, playing with the countertransference to see what my images may reveal about my reactions to him. I begin to see him as the more seasoned staff sees him: entrenched and hopeless in his patterns played out over years of counseling in this agency. I pause my reactivity and wonder how I can generate compassion, and even let go of the fear that I could be like him under other circumstances–this is a fear that evokes a cold dread in me. I wonder if this is the shadow side of compassion, a recognition that ultimately we are all in the same boat. Before beginning my internship I created a pale watercolor image of myself standing at the back of a boat, looking through a telescope across the water. Which way was I traveling, forward or backwards, I wondered.

Standing in my own studio, I bring my mind back to my client and create response art in the form of a series of portraits of my client. I make bold strokes in thick black ink on the gel plate, capturing his angular features. I make a single print, then work back into the plate, allowing the imagined and remembered portrait of him to change by adding more lines and rubbing others out. Each of the six impressions reveals a different face. Whose face is it? His? Mine? I am trying to help myself by letting him be outside of my impressions and assumptions this way, externalizing my image of him, watching it evolve and change, even disappear as I print a ghost impression before cleaning off the plate.

He never returns to the clinic, although his name flashes across my mind weekly as I toggle through my computerized caseload program still loaded with his profile. It seems the only art therapy I will do with him will be in response to our work together. I have learned to leave a little prayer for him as his name fades into the next one appearing on the screen.

It is challenging, if even possible, to create experiences with actual clients at the same level I was able to in the academic setting. Though I would not have characterized my art therapy preparations for previous clients and peers as relaxed, at least I had the luxury of researching each encounter based in a theoretical approach using directives from various texts. I am finding the pace and culture of this agency demand the simple approach of laying out a variety of drawing materials on a stiff-backed pad of paper to travel with me from room to room. Though the art therapy room offers a reasonable setting to paint and make things (a glass covered table provides a large work surface and facilitates easy clean-up), the other rooms have minimal if any table space, and materials must migrate with me from room to room. I find I must anticipate my needs ahead to have the set up ready. I am beginning to appreciate the capacity and simplicity of a single line to predict and convey the direction of an entire session.

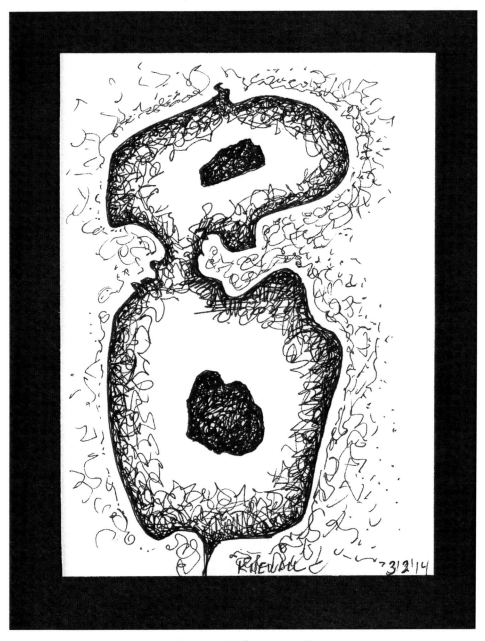

Figure 6. "Differentiation."

Winter

It is not the beginning anymore and I tell myself it doesn't need to be so hard. My path can be easier and I remind myself that makes the paths of my clients easier as well.

I am going through my usual dance of negotiation: replaying in my head comments I made during class case consult. Ego gets me coming and going: either I am too invisible or I am talking too much and showing off. I enjoyed a delicious walk to the beach after my eight-hour day at school and was able to step away from my habitual self-flagellation to simply take in the quiet, the colors, the edge of cold and the beckoning sunset that urged my dog-friend Basho and me to run the last downhill leg of our walk, giving me a few moments to sit and sing to the day's end as the sun's final sliver fell into a blue cloud bank. The cold dusk was a second companion on the slow climb back to the warmth of my friend's home, where I stay between internship days. The slow tree-obscured ascent of the swelling moon kept me company in the hot tub; later, the glowing sky saturated the silent lawn.

Something is opening in me. My own art practice has been dormant for a long time. Except for the course assignments and the drawing I do as I teach my elementary school students in my role as resident artist, it has been years since I was actively developing along my own creative course as a visual artist. My current impetus to draw comes as I engage a school assignment to make art in response to my first quarter of internship. Clearing the disarray and spreading out my printmaking supplies, I decide to hold my clients in mind and see what emerges while playing with new monoprint techniques. Although I am holding one client more consciously in mind, the portrait I am creating in multiple images, is a portrait of a different woman. In each successive print, I see her evolving from child to adolescent, to young adult, and finally to the woman she is now. None of this was conscious on my part. I wonder if I can even show these images because they are so clearly her face and I know they were done while thinking of someone else. What kind of communication is this? Ultramarine blue slides around the border of the printing plate as she moves into adulthood and fades as she ages; she is now looking at me through multiple images and selves. Where will this take us?

My client reports a dream. It was a dream of peace. Looking out a window, she saw—familiar yet unknown to her—a bucolic scene she did not recognize but which evoked a sense of calm. I thought to myself: "This is huge. Isn't peace the very thing everyone seeks? Hasn't she achieved it?" Yet there seems to be something else she measures success by, as though this dream is secondary to another end she seeks.

She is now reluctant to make art in our sessions and I am compelled to explore my internalization of her in my studio. I create a series of portraits

Figure 7. "Breaking open."

on the gel plate. A series of faces emerge through subsequent printing that reveal a woman who appears in her twenties and who ages with each fresh impression from the plate until a fairly accurate, recognizable portrait of her current age appears. This progression of images is how I hold her story and development within me. I feel the intimacy of our sessions, her reluctant revelations, and her ambivalence as she slowly turns toward herself in what seems to be unfamiliar and new ways. The eyes in the portraits I have done look fully ahead; I feel the weight, color, and temperature of her stories as they have entered my inner world—here they reside. I recall asking an art therapist guest lecturer, how he deals with holding the images of the artwork of the killers he studies and he replied, "I play with my kids a lot." My client strikes me as fairly typical in some ways, yet the intensity of her life is still enough to elicit this intense response in me.

At the end of this session, she cancels again and again and finally says she will "take a break" and maybe return later. I feel disappointment and I wonder how or if I could have enticed her to stay. Did I push too much? Did too much emerge too quickly? I know I am taking this personally, but I can't help it. I wonder about the state of her snake phobia, whether she has shed some skin of fear, and whether her peaceful dream has infiltrated her life.

Despite my client's departure from art therapy, I end this day satisfied. That is common for me and I know that I love doing this work even when my doubts are exploding, there is a little place of peace. I have a stillness in my center that confirms my growing art therapist identity. This client has shown me the power of a single, tense resistant line to draw out the deep places.

A teenage girl remembers she was told that at birth her twin died and she lived. When she was three, her mother died of an infected finger caused during a routine hospital visit. Since that age she has been afraid something is conspiring to kill her—a fluke disease, a random germ? Who can blame her? She is in frequent contact with the Centers for Disease Control to find out the latest information about disease and is a frequent contributor to a blog about anxiety. She claims anxiety as her central identity, and further elaborates her descriptions of what sounds like hypochondria.

Her hand has become infected. A red line runs up her arm and the school nurse seeing it calls Child Protective Services to report suspected medical neglect. Her father refused to get her treatment and she blames herself for trying to take care of it herself and for making it worse. Their relationship is strained and I wonder if this serious drama is being enacted now that she has a place in our art therapy sessions for her trauma to surface and play out.

I see her the next day. The negativity in her home is growing. It could form into something bad, she says, and I see real fear in her eyes. I am tempted to argue with her, telling her it will be OK, but I see she is showing me a deeper level to her fear in the mandala drawings. She is afraid that something could form from the negativity that is growing around her. She is an adolescent who hates and loves her father and wants to run away to an idealized retreat with relatives in a far-off state. She leaves the session early; I ask for her to stay a bit longer, but she won't. As she goes, she suggests the very directive I would have made: she says she will draw her anger into a rage notebook at home. This intention never materializes and the art she creates happens only in our sessions.

A New Year

My client with domestic abuse difficulties has been in the same situation for months. Now, however, she says she is open to leaving despite her unanswered questions and lack of guarantees for her future. I have learned to sit with her as she continues to lock herself in her room bolted against this odd man she had hoped would offer her a new life. Instead of safety, she has lost her affordable housing and seeks emergency lodging daily—so far without success. I know there is a bigger story here, but up to now, I haven't been told the larger patterns and I focus my attention on my image of my client as a chanting Hindu woman with a vision to bring a home of peace into the world and who can see her altar dominant in her home once again. If she could only sing this vision past doubts and the gravity of her past trauma, she would never trade it in again.

Meanwhile, I ask her to teach me her way of praying so I, too, can hold the light of her vision and help it to grow. When she chants aloud, I see a yellow tone carried through eons travelling like a river of gold through the office we sit in together—I have never heard anything like it. Is this what a "lifestream" looks like and sounds like? What is it she might be learning this time around? As I see her light brighten, the air thickens—there must be a tipping point, a decision to move in one direction more than another. Could she have made a decision to stop cleaning up the shit of others? Keep curious, I tell myself, and listen carefully.

I ask her to draw her life as she wishes it to be and she settles in with fine tipped markers to render a two story house by the sea. Its brightly lit windows feature family members smiling inside. The ocean is in view and lovely green trees shade the scene. A weak smile crosses her face; it looks like relief from her current traumatic life. In another picture, she paints an angel with yellow wings. Could this image be about her voice and the energy she is able to conjure in her spiritual practice?

As the weeks pass, she seems to relish the feel of the polymer clay she shapes as she speaks. She likes to tell her story and today she fashions a small container as her words spill out.

She will take a packet of clay with her to keep her company in her room during the hours she locks herself away from her abusive partner.

My teen client is the success I announce in school consultation group. In our last session, she reported that her anxiety is gone and she is happy. The faces she draws on her mandalas feature a wide grin. We share lunch in our small meeting room off the office at the local high school. I bring healthy salads to share. She asks about nutrition and says that she is researching the relationship between anxiety and nutrition on the internet. My supervisor warns, "She is attaching to you." Although I do not see myself as particularly maternal–at 55 I have no children of my own–still, he insists, "you are a mother figure to her."

Mainly, I listen as she impatiently talks above my reflections and questions. She wants so much to be heard! I am learning to observe and be silent to allow her innate desire to heal and grow find its expression. I keep a sheet of paper with a circle drawn on it on the table between us so she can respond silently with lines and colors and written words when she cannot speak.

My own anxiety about being enough, knowing enough, offering something of value–sometimes gets the better of me, but slowly, very slowly, I yield to my silent curiosity and trust in my client's own wisdom. I remind myself that I show up every week, am there when she arrives; that I am someone who cares and tries to be entirely present for her. I see the evidence of all that being a big thing for her–a container for her growth. I may be the only adult who quietly attends to her fears and frustrations. I understand that it is essential that she have a safe place to unfold under her own gaze and onto the drawing paper. I notice how I try to choose directives a client can accept, and for her, a simple, predictable, repeated ritual of the mandala circle provides continuity and comfort in our weekly sessions.

I hope perhaps she is seeing herself differently. The folder of her drawings is getting bigger and is evidence of her improvement and movement. The art provides a concrete place for her to arrive and be. Her folder of images will be available to her later as she reflects back on our time

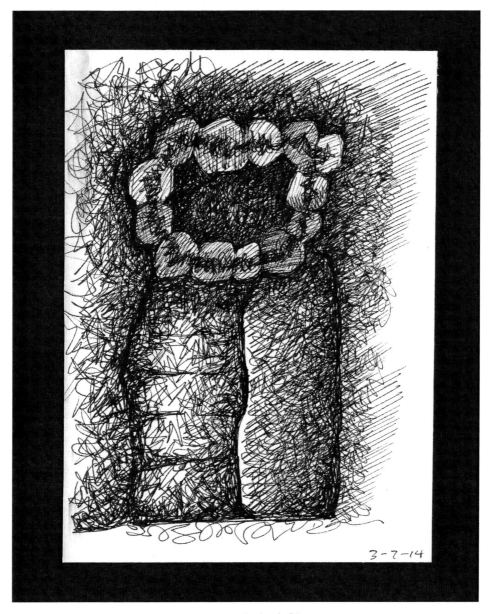

Figure 8. "Defended."

together. This is one of the gifts of art therapy, the art acts as alternative evidence for healing that competes with the gravity of maladaptive patterns that can take hold in the psyche. I hope I am not wrong, but she appears to me to be choosing to head in the direction of healing, and I think creating and reviewing her own visual commitment to herself has a profound effect. She smiles as she looks through the artwork. Although she doesn't offer words, I see she is pleased and relieved to be held within the collection of her images and within my careful collecting of her drawings.

As we reflect on her artwork, I notice that the large scared eyes she originally drew on her mandalas stayed constant over the months we worked together, although the mouths she drew would shift with her present mood, and provided an entry point for our discussions. The mandala templates passed between us, but I knew she was struggling to connect with me—when she wrote her answers to my questions, she wrote them upside-down, orienting her responses away from herself and toward me. The weekly mandalas have become a predictable ritual and transitional object as well as a document of her progress. Over our time together, I notice she has relaxed more and her anxieties subsided. She appears relieved of her debilitating compulsion to scour her world for threats, her focus has shifted to healthy eating and increased exercise, and she begins to describe her healing rather than her pending illness.

During our last session, she examines her early drawings and seems satisfied with what she has achieved. Her focus is shifting to excitement now about traveling to see relatives across the country. As we end, I watch her describe the return of "my anxiety" as she calls it, as though it is a kind of difficult friend never too far off, waiting in the wings for her attention. My supervisor tells me the return of an original symptom at termination is natural and to be expected. But I am worried. Her anxiety may always live in the empty outline of her mother who died when she was so young. As the school year ends and we have our last session together, I notice a round red spot on the same hand as her previous infection. She tells me she is struggling with guilt over the rupture in her relationship with her father caused by the tension of an earlier call to Children's Protective Services.

I ask about the mark on her hand; she smiles and seems pleased I have noticed it. I worry that as we end our time together, this mark is a signal that all is not well. I think she might be turning her anger on herself and I am concerned about letting her leave. I gently remind her she is not at fault for the Children's Protective Services call, but she is caught in a looping rumination. The mandala she draws is a face caught between a smile and a frown, with small black dots for eyes. She has refused my efforts to bring her father into therapy and here my hands are tied.

I wonder what she will choose to bring to herself in the months to come, and whether we will continue our work together when school resumes in the fall. I watch her leave the room stiffly, not so unlike the way she entered on her first day. She leaves her folder of mandalas, poetry, and lists for my safe-keeping. I sit alone in the small conference room, looking once again at her stack of drawings—evidence of time and feelings and secret messages passed between us. I have seen much more of her because of the drawings and somehow she knows this. In them, she revealed a fear of her father she could barely admit to, she listed her hopes, and she grappled to identify her feelings. In the end, she could see the territory she had crossed in her art and I think in the end she was impressed with her own self-healing.

Spring

Max says art therapy "is the best thing" and I am willing to be convinced. My easy use of art throughout my own healing journey did not always fit with what I currently do in the sessions I conduct. It is tougher to get art therapy clients to make art. My clients are not professional artists and are generally uncomfortable with my request that they show me, rather than tell me, what's going on for them. Even when they have the experience of seeing a simple image they make reveal, and therefore predict, the entire unfolding of a session, they still hesitate to make art the next time. Despite this, I invite them to use the materials to make something.

Perhaps it is exactly because they have experienced what art can reveal that they avoid it. Perhaps on some level they feel it makes them vulnerable on many fronts: first, most people feel inadequate in "art" no matter how many times they are reassured art therapy is about image not art. Perhaps we should change the name "art therapy." Is it confusing? Should we adopt the term "expressive arts"[3] to soften and broaden the specificity of the request and thereby diffuse performance anxiety? Would changing the name help? Or, as Max says, is performance anxiety a natural manifestation of resistance?

I direct my client to heavy watercolor paper. After first covering the page with barely visible dirty white squiggles, she begins her signature spiral right of center, emerging from flowing, saturated color. She dry brushes each stroke as it makes its way toward the center of the page. She talks

---

3. Editor's note: The term "expressive arts" is typically used to denote a variety of the arts such as dance, movement, music along with the visual arts in therapy. Some art therapists (e.g., McNiff & Robbins) designate themselves "expressive" therapists. There is also a national professional organization called "Expressive Arts Association" which is different from the American Art Therapy Association.

as she paints, her story unwinding itself as she works, comforted perhaps by the hand's gestures and the pleasures of mark-making.

My client's pain and shame travel wordlessly alongside her rather detached description of a recent doctor's appointment. Eventually, she makes a connection between trauma from a rape she suffered in childhood and the invasive medical procedure of this week, which interestingly she came to see as a reenactment and a healing of the past trauma. Her painted spiral brings the story from the center of the page into the room and she draws a pale blue tinted heart standing watch in a sky of tainted white; she titles it "Striking a Balance."

In our next session, she deftly applies a shape of water to the textured paper and fills the liquid with bright orange, then yellow, until an elegant daffodil appears. Soon a garden fills the page with multiple flowers leaning into a brilliant blue sky. Her typical way of coping with intense transitions and unknowns in her life has been to create, move, tend, describe, and activate herself in an attempt to distract from the oncoming trauma at hand. Dropping into the beauty of her own making in the watercolor allows her the chance to sit with the complexity of her life. She is able to see the gentle emergence of patterns and past events that sit below her activity and which pull her energy into depression.

When she leaves the office that day, she shows me photographs of daffodils she has been taking. She moves naturally toward beauty in times of pain; her resiliency is fostered as she creates in our session.

"I really believe in this art stuff," she reports: "I didn't know it was so powerful." In session, she paints a layered heart. A rainbow of contoured edges border the heart with a red-purple center safely encased in thick painted lines. Surrounding the outlined heart is a bright cheery yellow. She does not paint the lower right corner. There, a gray-blue patch completes the background.

She says she does terrible things she has no recollection of and begins to cry. I am listening and watch her draw an armored heart on the paper. It will not be until later that I think clearly about her words to me. I realize I may have not really taken them in so I don't have to believe or disbelieve.

I have heard many horrible things from clients and I wonder where do these horrible things "go" in me? Tightness spreads over my chest and I find it hard to breathe. My client has applied for temporary disability and I wonder if that application requires me to share my case notes with other agencies—so many things to really understand about confidentiality. This

Figure 9. "Breathe."

line of thought causes a tightening in my eyes, and I begin to swallow more. I feel a restless irritation with my lack of knowledge and a familiar self-judgment creeps over me: I know this creepy feeling all too well.

Anxiety builds with my awareness of ignorance. I should know more, do more! I use my awareness of this line of thought to breathe more deeply and detach from my client's escalating and dramatic storyline. I am left with a competing desire to believe what she tells me and at the same time, not believe, and I have a desire to wash over both options with some kind of compelling distraction. I go get myself another cup of coffee. The best perk in the agency is an expensive Italian espresso machine and we can have all the free coffee we choose to consume.

But my heart begins to tighten more; her painted lines disguised as rainbow layers have become metal bands around my own heart. I breathe again and walk outside, around the building away from the windows of offices. I look into the quivering alder tree as wind agitates the leaves and a graying sky chills my bare skin. It doesn't feel like the beginning of summer, and I call up energy from the earth and pull down sky energy to help to ground my own small self.

I have two child clients who come late in the afternoon and I struggle to learn their language of thought and emotion. Sometimes they will draw with me or create scenes in the sandtray.[4] One day, the little boy painted a deliberate rainbow. He requested two large sheets of paper in his usual way, asking for more until I set a limit. I am struck by his rainbow: it has an open bottom edge and a mountainous quality. He has also made a cave with traps inside.

He was brought to the clinic to help him with anxiety brought on by a pending move across the country. He sometimes describes his life: "My father caught 20 bad guys," he says. "That's a lot of bad guys," I say. He spent his first few sessions adding water to the sandtray until I said it was too much. Limits? He experimented with the sand's saturation point and tested my willingness to turn the wood tray into a pool. Now we toss the football and he throws it until I say "that is too hard for me." Like the girl I see after him, he sets rules for our soccer games that change frequently.

I complain at internship meetings that I never know if I am "doing therapy" when I see kids. I feel insecure with my understanding of developmental stages although I have taught art in elementary schools to all grades for 20 years. I study a sheet of case note examples that reference

---

4. "Sandtray" or "sandplay" is akin to play therapy with children. It is based on the theories of C. G. Jung and is non-verbal and symbolic. In a therapy room, miniature figures are available to use in a tray full of sand. Water can be added. Dora Kalff is known as the founder of sandplay. Although it is not only for children, a sandtray is found in many therapy rooms where children are clients. Some of the first proponents of sandtray in the United States gave workshops on the technique in the Pacific Northwest.

the psychological equivalents of play such as "client used movement to express emotions physically and engaged in metaphoric play to make meaning of his experience." OK, that helps. These examples are legitimate adult language seeking both to understand a child's messages and to satisfy managed care. I am starting to get the hang of the notes.

Summer

One intern remarks: "Research shows therapists do not feel competent until three to five years into practice." I feel horrified and relieved. My supervisor reminds me "It takes a long time to get good at this, just be with your client." I am grateful my supervisor prioritizes presence over protocol. Blending in the necessary paperwork as a parallel process to the listening and reflecting has been a slow accrual of skills for me.

Lately, I have felt relieved when I listen to the struggles of the other interns, especially the one who is a newer arrival at the clinic than I am. Soon, six new arrivals will fill the small agency competing for rooms, bringing their excitement and anxiety into the little buildings we hustle through. I will be the experienced one who pauses to check in with them and assists them with all the new charting, case notes, and scheduling questions. I begin to realize what it will be like as I choose to continue here after graduation as an extern. The handful of clinic staff holds the anchor for a continual influx of new energy flowing through.

My case load is continually shifting leaving folders of client artwork behind. My portfolio is stuffed with paintings and drawings, bulging with the occasional mask-in-process. I thumb though the images as I wait for my next client. My office window faces the agency's small parking lot and I see her park in front of the building, then watch her slowly walk toward the lobby entrance. I feel slightly voyeuristic as I examine her unobserved. But I tell myself I am collecting useful data. I see her gait is slow and she walks with a slight limp. A fluid, hot sensation drops almost imperceptibly into my belly and I realize I am sickened by imagining what her daily experience must be like. Is she always sick? What must that be like for her? Stretching toward the level of empathy that would breach my defenses sounds the alarm of irritation first, then a dismissive anger, then I just breathe and collect myself as she enters the lobby and signs in.

My office has become a sanctuary to me. I consider, the space I work out of to be a crucial collaborator in the healing process. Art therapist Shaun McNiff writes about the studio space as the central component of

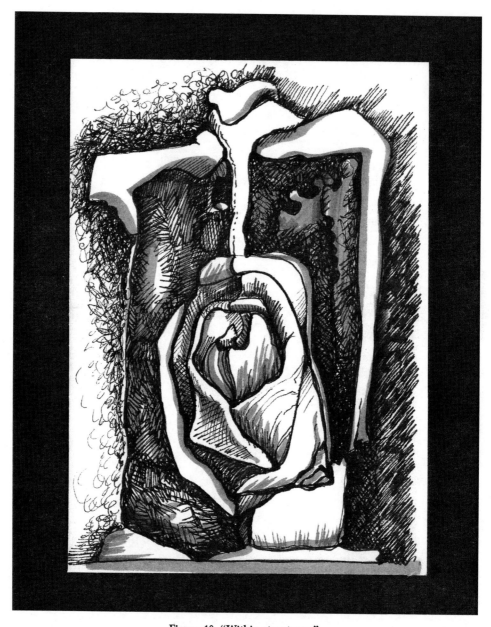

Figure 10. "Within structures."

the therapeutic process, along with materials and the leader's ability to hold the healing container. Rather than a genesis myth, that states "In the beginning was the symptom," McNiff writes, "art therapy might try imagining itself from a non-medical perspective of 'in the beginning was the space'" (McNiff, 2004, p. 26).[5]

The previous art therapist fashioned the room with care and beauty. After her departure from the clinic, I immediately felt the threat of encroachment by staff and interns desperate for a room in an agency always short on office space. This was my first public act of embracing my distinct art therapist identity and stepping into the responsibility of continuing a tenuous legacy. I borrowed soothing quilts from my mother's studio and went about asking others for their input and permission to install them. Staff members commented on my "laying claim" and I agreed, yes, I was. This space should be dedicated to art therapist staff and interns.

My client is particularly attuned to the aesthetics in the room. She complains about the dreary colors in one quilt, and the filled-up check-in canvas, spontaneous and chaotic, hanging to her right. She is accustomed to the more orderly bright colors of her previous home and is having a tough time acclimatizing to the very different forest green and array of grays of the Pacific Northwest.

This is her first session with me since telling me she has other parts of herself which act out in terrible ways without her knowledge. She is afraid it will continue to happen, and the guilt she feels for the pain she has brought to her family and especially her husband, eats at her. She struggles with this debilitating guilt that drives her perfectionist approach to everything she does. She is depressed, yet presents as manically enthusiastic, continually describing the exhausting amount of activities she generates for her kids and herself. I wonder how she manages.

Although I question if I should, it is the clinic's custom and I usually end up calling her when she doesn't arrive for her session on time. Her voice is flat when she answers her phone, as though she doesn't know me, or why I am calling. I wonder if her strange voice reflects a delay as she tries to remember if she had an appointment or was she asleep?

This day she arrives at the office in a bright mood, apologetic, energetic, with a vibrant laugh. I place a paper with the circle on the table and she asks "Why a circle?" I respond by saying it is called a "mandala," Sanskrit for circle; it represents the wholeness of the self, as well as being a container for the image, I say, although you don't need to stay in the lines.

---

5. McNiff, S. (2004). *Art heals: How creativity cures the soul.* Boston: Shambala.

Lately, a result of the rich dialogue I have with Maxine, I am directing (rather than asking) clients to create mandalas to show me what is going on for them. I am good-natured as I ignore resistance and complaints. Then I look at the mandalas my clients draw through the lens of the "MARI"[6] identifying the overall image within the context of colors and symbols based on the work of Carl Jung, and organized according to stages of change. Maxine has encouraged me to focus the work of each session on the client's images, and to allow the natural unfolding of the session to determine subsequent images, allowing the therapy to go deeper as a result.

The mandala my client draws begins with small inward-moving spirals drawn within the confines of the circle. Then she draws spirals that move outward. I recall her first drawings were larger spirals alternating between inward and outward movements as well. She picks up two oil pastels in her hand and makes double line spring shapes moving in and out of the circle covering the whole surface. She announces she usually only uses rainbow colors but in this drawing she is combining colors that are new for her. Once again I recall she held two or three pastels in her hand to make her first images months ago when we began working together. I review the stages of change in the MARI assessment and it says the spiral is associated with initiating and activation. She titles her drawing "Springs."

I become a detective, reading into her image multiple interpretations based on publications I have found correlating research. I feel excited that I might have a way to approach this difficult situation. They say art is uniquely suited to evoke unconscious states, and can offer a safe way to access aspects of the self. Art therapy can also offer evidence of a fractured self. Using the client's own images may give her a sense of control.

I am excited as I consider this approach centered on confirming pathology and attempting to solve it. McNiff claims that using art merely as a projective tool to decipher pathology is reductionist and destructive (McNiff, 2004, p. 32).[7] I consider letting my client's springs bounce free rather than hold her in a static form that keeps a diagnosis in place. I am constantly resisting the urge to fit in pathology-finding mode of treatment. Do I really trust in the power of the image as both evidence and instigator of its own intelligent self-healing? I see how making multiple images in a

---

6. "MARI" stands for Mandala Assessment Research Instrument created by Joan Kellogg in 1980. Kellogg, J. (1984). *Mandala: Path of Beauty.* Belleair, FL: ATMA, Inc.

7. McNiff, S. (2004). *Art heals: How creativity cures the soul.* Boston: Shambala.

single session allows transformation to happen; the multiple images flow like water, cleansing by flowing-through.

After completing her drawing, she begins to talk about her guilt. I ask her where guilt is in her body, and she places her hand over her heart. I then ask her to drop into her heart, and she begins to cry. I acknowledge her disclosures of the previous session and assure her she can bring her full self here, into the art, into this room. She says "this has been a good place for me." She appears relieved. Her speech has slowed down, and her body appears more relaxed.

I have a lot to learn: I am concerned that I am objectifying my client through what I have read. Am I reducing her to symptoms and characteristics of a diagnosis? On one hand, I feel the excitement of a scientist ready for dissection, wanting to close in around the precision of words to attain a sense of knowing something important. On the other hand, I want to go another direction–toward the mystery of what is already in the process of being transformed through the spaciousness of the image. There is so much energy in what is being activated and released. I don't want to become wedded to a description of illness which may be moving into a new form. Even calling it an illness may deny the wisdom of a brilliant defense. What I can provide are the materials and space for change; that's what I want to get excited about.

The day started rough. I felt anxious from the beginning. This was my first supervision session since my supervisor returned from vacation. Was my fear in anticipation of the day? I sometimes feel caught in hiding–I have learned that voicing my general discomfort to staff or myself only undermines my self-esteem and presents me as less capable. It seems more helpful to move into the details of a case. Instead of telling my supervisor: "everything is scaring me today," I play the recording of the session I've brought in. The fear in me rises as the audio continues and my supervisor says "so you want help with this?" The client on the tape reports a seemingly endless stream of terrible experiences–one setback after another. I play the tape because I don't want to hold her story alone. As I watch my supervisor's face, I see he is completely absorbed in his listening. I wish he would see how hard it is for me to hold this, but he has stepped into my client's world, not mine, and will offer me an approach. He says: "you do too much with her, slow down". Then he demonstrates simple questions like "what's it like to feel that?" or "you are really strong to have survived." He offers the same advice he has offered before to me: "You let yourself

Figure 11. "Exhaustion and hope."

get too worried about your clients–that does not help them. You won't last as a therapist if you don't learn how to detach."

This woman has made many images in our sessions. She often chooses the mandala paper with the circle preprinted on it. Her images sometimes morph into birds: the eye she drew last time, she said, was the eye of a policeman; then, strangely, it became a tender feathered bird head. One time before, she made a small clay vessel that featured a single wing. Today she tells me she'd like to take her children to her mother's house and fly away from her life.

Today, I feel like I am on a small boat alone on choppy waters and I am landing on one small island after another. I walk into the art therapy room and quickly put materials on the table, breathe for a moment, watch the clock until I can time my entrance into the waiting room precisely on the hour and invite my client onto our island.

At eight months into the internship, I can feel myself becoming looser, more curious, accepting that I can't know what will happen or what wants to happen. I feel more able to assume art will occur despite resistance, and I am experiencing less resistance as a result. This particular week I put out the collage materials. I tear pictures from magazines making sure there are a variety of kinds of images: people, landscapes, and objects that catch my eye. My choosing starts collaboration.

The middle-aged woman who struggles to keep her interest in life comes in for her second session. She says she collects wood to construct unique pieces of sculpture. She cares for her grown son and fears for his safety; she wants to be free of him and yet she wants him near. Her boyfriend has recently left her broken-hearted and the weight of all of this causes her to imagine that death might bring her peace.

She is actually excited to see my box of collage images. This is so rare that clients welcome the art-making that I notice an unfamiliar lift in my heart and I think "oh it's nice when this feels easy!" My client exclaims, "I love collage! I keep a stack of magazines by my bed stand!" I ask "When is the last time you made a collage?" "Five years ago," she replies. She sorts decisively through the images placing and gluing as she shares the things she loves with me, reminded of them as she selects her pictures. I notice that no spaces are left between the pasted down pictures but I don't comment, and she says "I don't like to leave white spaces." She smiles as she shares her life while making her collage. Her eyes twinkle, then mist over as a sad story emerges from one of the magazine fragments. The glue bottle I have is defective and there are no glue sticks in the room. She cheerfully removes the malfunctioning top and deftly pours glue onto the back of each torn image spreading it evenly with another piece of paper. She is not easily frustrated; she can make it work and hardly misses a beat dealing with this glitch. I realize later I could have pointed this out. Maxine's

pithy slogan "everything has meaning" stays with me and makes the awkward moments, when I am not prepared or things don't go smoothly, alive
opportunities to discover how my clients handle difficulties. She has no
title for her artwork, and we agree to talk about it more next week. She
wants to leave it with me.

My teenage client finally opened up last week. When she spotted the
magazines and calendars something seemed to come alive in her. She sat
on the floor looking, choosing images, and putting them back. I asked, "do
you like photography?" She shows me image after image on her phone:
adventures from a recent trip. I speak of her sensitivity to textures and
sources of light, how her images move from foreground to middle ground
to background. She smiles, but says just a few words here and there to give
her pictures context. There are skateboards and images of super heroes,
which she carefully draws in pencil alongside a timeline of her life, documenting the many moves she's made. I notice the small circular scars that
dot her hands, cigarette burns? Afraid of pushing her away, I don't ask. I
think about that decision all week.

This week I look harder for the scars, small scratches, brighter red. I
have a lot of time to watch her hands as she sorts slowly through the collage box. I resist the urge to offer more images as she seems to have a hard
time finding any she likes. I am too uncomfortable with discomfort! I stay
with my discomfort and make myself watch how she works. Finally, she
finds three collage pictures she likes, a pocket watch, two children in a
dark room their faces lit from below ("ghost stories" kept going through
my mind," she says), and an astronaut shown from the back floating away
into black space. A picture of a liquor shelf in sepia tones is selected in the
first round than put back only to be pulled out again later. Cyclists passing
by a large column survive cull after cull. She requests black paper and
keeps going back to the box. She resorts, puts images back, selects them
again, and adds new ones. She keeps only a few out at a time. We sit in
silence. At one point, I couldn't help myself and I put out two magazines
with what I thought would be more interesting images for a teenager. She
ignored them.

Her fingers move the images slowly around on the black paper. She
carefully trims the edges of each picture and even methodically attempts
to cut out the small ovals of background between the links in the pocket
watch's small chain. Unable to manage it, she snips off the chain altogether, smiling, unphased. I offer time checks about how much time is left in
our session. Instead of gluing her composition down, she requests a paper-

Figure 12."Opening."

clip, carefully stacks her selections together and clips them to the black construction paper. We agree she'll continue next week.

I am struck by her patience and persistence. I wonder how her aesthetic sense has developed as it seems unusually sophisticated to me. She has a passion for image, texture, and patterns. I also discover her wounds. She may be hurting herself or being hurt by someone else. My client has been recently involved in inpatient treatment for her violent outbursts. In her involvement with the collage process, I see no indication at all of her rage.

I meet with my client's mother and she tells me her own story. My sense is that she also has a trauma history. I wonder how far to go with this and gently inquire if she has a therapist herself; she says she does not and that worries me. She says she tries to provide a lot of family structure for her child who likely has Reactive Attachment Disorder. After the session, the mother calls me often and I have had to set limits on phone contact. My supervisor has advised that I focus my work with my client on identity development rather than attempting to facilitate better attachment with her mother.

She brings new drawings each week; does she do this to please me? Is that OK? She shares her music, digital images, and songs with me—she is bursting with creativity; her words are few, she does not discuss her feelings yet, and shrugs off my questions. Carefully shaded portraits of her idols, cartoons, and well-crafted photographs populate our hours together.

Late Summer

The 30-year-old Indian woman struggles with her recent break up and seems stuck in the behaviors of a twenty-something. This is our tenth session and she is concerned her depression is not improving; she sees her ex-partner daily. She lives in a small town and the two of them still travel in a tight circle of friends. My client blames herself for the couple's problems and is struggling to set boundaries to help her move on. She speaks about wanting family and I ask her to draw what that looks like for her. She gives me that smile that says "I don't want to, but it is too hard to refuse you so I will" and she leans back on the couch, hunches over the paper with markers by her side. She is finally able to start when I ask her to pull out a color that seems right. I cannot see what she is drawing. She continues to speak softly about the pain of a relationship she is trying to end; her confusion and ambivalence ignite with each encounter along with an irresistible pull to find comfort in familiar places.

The session is coming to a close and I ask to see her image. She has drawn a small figure. Its head is a circle with a slit opening in the center; it looks behind itself. The body is made of short stick-figure lines. Two lines extend from the slit in the head and open in a 'v' shape to enclose a large yellow flower form. This is the second time she has shown herself with a partial face. I ask if some part of the picture is her and she claims she is the little figure looking back. She has neither title nor words to offer about her picture. I suggest we start with it next week.

This woman grew up in a collectivist culture and was expected to conform to strict gender roles. She was raped by a man in her teens who was more powerful than her parents who were not willing to challenge him to protect her. She has found her freedom in the United States, married a man she has since divorced, and is now raising her young son. She is struggling to establish her identity. Saying "no" and setting her own course runs counter to her earlier cultural conditioning. She knows how to leave when things get too bad, but not how to stay present and state her needs. The figure in her drawing has no face; perhaps she has lost face and cannot yet see who she is. In another recent drawing, she has filled a mandala with a symmetrical tree form firmly rooted to the bottom of the circle. Our sessions are less about her "ex" now, and she has started to imagine her future. The colors in her latest mandala are as intense and clear as her eyes are becoming.

One of my teen clients is 16 years old and I have seen her three times when she draws the mandala for me. With the background I already have, I begin to identify the components of her image and see the color references to mother issues and to fragmentation. The MARI assessment indicates a deeper wounding than I see in her defensive adolescent nonchalance. Her yawns and bored sideways glances cover a life of abandonment by a mentally-ill mother. I am new at this assessment, but I am amazed that the colors she has chosen and the forms she has drawn all point to the issues I am already aware of, and suggest further inquiry into areas I don't yet understand. Her image points to a person who has had to parent herself, and this is accurate for her. I feel elated that perhaps this art therapy assessment system can assist me to decipher my client's nonverbal communications.

Suddenly I feel awakened out of a complacency I didn't realize I was falling into. I recognize the community mental health system I am working in calls out to serve as many individuals as is humanly possible, and these heroics are rewarded with phrases like "you are a rock star!" The time to reflect and plan for a particular client is limited and not considered as essential as logging in the hours of direct client contact. My weekly supervision is commonly limited to one or two clients on my 15-client caseload which leaves many questions unasked and unanswered. I am at the agency three days a week loading as many appointments as possible to acquire the needed hours amidst the many no-shows common to community mental health. It is summer now and suddenly schedules change, child clients disappear, and adults feel better with the warmer weather and head out on vacations. The temptation to take on new clients competes with the need to keep slots open for the erratic ones. I spend time daily with the puzzle of my schedule; post-it notes migrate over the grid of hours in my day-planner and get finalized in the computer version online. Still people arrive at random times, and often not at all. Changing gears quickly to maximize my time, I am tempted to complete case notes during the abandoned sessions. The materials sit waiting, the preparations, internal and external, are suspended. There is a period of time when the person may still arrive and the container of our work together is in place. Fifteen minutes into our session, I will call my absent client to check-in, remind, reschedule.

To jump in with efficiency, opening the case note program, engaging with another life instead of just sitting with my as yet absent client is too abrupt, takes me out of myself. I know Maxine would encourage me to see this no-show as the session itself trying to understand "what is happening here?" In this space without the client, I make a piece of response art: explore the feeling of sitting with the fading expectation as it shifts to a feeling of rejection (is it me? Did I do something wrong last week?), disappointment, maybe relief that I can avoid that person's pain and difficult life in this hour and rest instead. Annoyance at another missed hour in my necessary accrual for graduation, the stress that underlies that dynamic: no face-to-face, no credit. The massive amounts of free labor graduate students donate to the survival of this particular agency is one thing, I can reframe this as my personal social justice project; however, to dismiss the preparation, availability, and follow-up required for each scheduled appointment when a client doesn't arrive adds unreasonable stress on me. This dynamic filters into the therapeutic relationship as I watch myself scrutinize potential clients by their track record of missed appointments. I become more ruthless about this as I head into my final quarter, keeping close count of accumulated hours and my graduation date. I look forward to being relieved of this layer of concern as my internship comes to a close.

Fall Returns

The summer is over and my case consult class at the university meets for the last time. In these three-hour blocks, I felt held and nurtured. I heard about the experiences of other student interns at sites and with clients different than mine, and I learned how other supervisors and agencies conducted business. These meetings were like a sanctuary where theory was finally infiltrated by our personal case studies and we grappled with real pain and trauma and the realization of what we had really gotten ourselves into. I was especially moved by the ways I watched and heard my colleagues and me begin our practice. These were our first days of being art therapists, and we were the witnesses of one another's dreams coming true. I will carry with me the memories of our tears of frustration as well as joy and deep empathy, the laughter at our attempts and mistakes, and especially the generosity of presence we held for one another. I will never be a beginner like this again.

As I gather my books into my bag I am aware of the surreal vividness of each detail in the room. My breath catches slightly in my throat as I hold back the full awareness of losing everything I am about to leave behind. The door closes behind me and I listen to the sound of my footsteps merging with the ambient conversations of the other students amplified as I move through the building for my final exit. I climb into my car and my mind moves in a new direction, no longer pulled between student and intern. I have been hired at the agency where I did my internship and I feel the responsibility of stepping forward to keep art therapy established there. I notice I have become like the woman I met with a year ago in the coffee shop. I will be the one a new art therapy intern takes to coffee, asking for support.

Afterward

My first act as a graduate is to install the drawings I made over the past year in the university gallery. I exit as an artist and a new art therapist. I work with the university art curator to hang nearly 100 pen and ink drawings at eye level along a curving wall as a timeline of my art therapist development. Each image documents a point in time in my internship, beginning the week before I started at the agency to the day I became staff. Like clouds shifting in the sky, each image is a culmination of self and environment.

Figure 13. "Growth."

Lights and darks move between foreground and background. Abstract forms morph into others, patterns emerge, and I offer the story to my coworker who has come to my opening. She speculates about one drawing in particular that looks chaotically dramatic, wondering if it corresponds to certain events at the agency. I wonder, too. As I graduate, I have entered a new art therapy community with its own unique dramas and routines as I exit the rich and fluctuating world of classes and coursework, deadlines and credits. I'm ready.

Chapter V

ART THERAPY STUDENT STORIES: WHAT WE ARE THINKING AND WHAT WE ARE FEELING

A book for and about students would not be complete without the voices of art therapy students. Here is that chapter of "student stories." We asked students in graduate programs across the country to describe their best and worst experiences and to tell us about their role models and the important qualities embodied by these people. We received a number of thoughtful answers to our queries and we are exceptionally grateful to the students who took the time and effort to answer our questions and to the program directors who gave permission for them to do it.

The following quotations represent students from a number of different art therapy programs, from various geographical areas in the United States. Although I have not formally taught in an art therapy program for a number of years, I was surprised to recognize the stories here as ones I know and have heard many times. Rather than unique to a particular program, I consider these stories to be universal reflections of the art therapist student's journey. Submissions have been edited and information which might identify a particular program or faculty member has been changed to ensure confidentiality.

Quotations Without Comments

What is your best experience?

Attending school part time has been key in my time management, but I've still struggled to balance my schedule between work, class, freelancing, practicum[1], supervision, and family.

My internship is in a nonprofit organization that conducts programs for children who are grieving the loss of a parent or sibling. Each child is assigned a "Big Buddy" who is an intern of their same gender. I felt like all of my worlds were intersecting. It's the same way I felt when I first discovered art therapy in my freshman year of college. Presented with the dilemma of whether to major in psych or fine art, my psychology 101 professor told me about art therapy and it was like a magical door to my future opened. It seems to me that the world of art therapy is such a connector, a community builder and that these moments of clarity and unity will continue over the course of my career.

Developing relationships with like-minded peers and faculty. I was not expecting to feel so close to my classmates . . . the women I have met through this program have transformed me.

Growing into what I believe it means to be an Art Therapist and to be comfortable in my skin as I try on that role has been challenging, terrifying, and exhilarating. I think the best experience that I've had has been getting to know myself through the process of classes, readings, internship, and my own therapy. I have grown in understanding of my own difficulties sitting with feelings and learning what it means to live in the "grey" areas of life: not only *existing* in the emotional and mental places that have no "true" or "false" answers, but *thriving* and taking up space.

Feeling a sense of connectedness and belonging in what I invest myself in and what I want to contribute to the world. In the art therapy program I feel that sense of belonging. I feel that I am fulfilling this need of mine to connect, contribute, and serve in a way that I am meant to. Finally, I found an area where I fit!

---

1. The words "practicum" and "internship" are used interchangeably.

I've had some wonderful self realizations . . . I began to see how distant I was from my emotions, that I intellectualized any emotion I experienced from others or myself. This led to my own journey of emotional reconnection which was painful but vastly liberating.

Looking at where I was three years ago, I think "holy cow, I hardly knew myself!" I feel that my graduate program, even with all of its faults, has provided the structure or "scaffolding" for me to use in fleshing out who I am as an art therapist, mental health worker, empathetic listener, container, space holder, pusher, puller, receiver, sister, daughter, friend, and myself.

My best experience happens each time I sit with someone and witness the discoveries that are made through art therapy. My practicum and internship work has focused on groups of 4–10, mostly men. Generally, art has not been a part of heir lives; in fact, most recall that they last used art materials as school children. There is hesitation to reach for a drawing instrument at first, but as the creative process draws the individual in, the story emerges. I feel privileged to be the first one to hear and see it. From my experience in that moment, I grow too. This is such rewarding work.

The most inspiring experiences I have had while in my program have been practicing art therapy. Through both of my internships, I have had the opportunity to witness firsthand the unique power of using the creative arts in therapy.

The way that art therapy has looked has been as diverse as the clients I have worked with at this point in my experience.

Some clients were extremely insightful about the meaning of their art. In one session, a young woman working to overcome an eating disorder talked extensively of the complicated feelings that she struggled with about her body. I asked if she was willing to draw her feelings out, and she proceeded to draw a powerful image: The image was a large hand drawing a small version of herself. Attached to the hand were strings that she said represented the pressures she felt from the outside world to be thin. The image at once solidified what she spoke of and served as a metaphor for her experience. Another client I worked with was limited verbally; I had the opportunity to simply witness the state of calm she settled into as she painted. I am constantly reminded in this work of the potential of art therapy to reflect one's inner experience and to guide the therapy process.

My best experience is the inner growth that happened in just this first year of art therapy education. I have been given the opportunity to really look and understand who I am and how I want to be an art therapist. What makes this journey even more unique is that I have not been alone because I have the support of 25 other students in my courses.

It's wonderful when you have a professor who has the passion alive in them.

Qualities I've learned? To be flexible and to feel I can't always control situations and that's ok. I learned that lending a compassionate, sincere, caring ear goes a long way and that sometimes being a witness without having to say anything can be very powerful. I have learned to really listen and be present with clients. I have also learned the importance of having at least some level of professional distance I learned when personal disclosure is appropriate and to discern when the desire to disclose is coming from my own needs. I hope I've learned to separate my own needs and find other ways and people to go to for my own issues. I have learned to give without needing anything back.

My best memory was during an experiential in our group psychotherapy class. In the class, we studied group therapy theory and also participated in a group training group (this component led the cohort to describe it as both the most celebrated and most hated class). The teacher led a directive to draw a dream and I was one of the six of the 22 students who elected to move into a smaller circle to discuss our drawings. After they were discussed, we chose one drawing, which happened to be mine, to reenact through a psychodrama technique. My dream involved a large log being pulled out of the water by ancient warriors in body armor and then the log transformed into a large warrior-robot creature that walked off. In the dream, I was hiding behind some grass watching the scene unfold in a large Greek style amphitheater overlooking the Mediterranean Sea. In class, each of the six people chose a part to enact, one was the log-turned-warrior, others were the warriors pulling the log out of the water, and a few people were the moving water. I watched from the corner of the room, as in the dream, and acted as "director." This experiential provided insights into my own transitions becoming an art therapist and my normal role as observer. This self-explorative process was amazingly pleasurable, both to have the experience of being witnessed by my cohort, to engage in a theatrical way of thinking and to have a fun process.

Some of the best experiences I've had have been towards the end of my third and last practicum. It's very hard to name *one* as the best, but what has been so rewarding is to finally feel like I have *become an art therapist*–that I've been able to apply the knowledge of the process and make it my own. In my last week of the practicum (I was working at an inpatient rehab hospital), I worked with a 90-year-old woman who said she hadn't painted for two years since she fell and broke her hip. Before that she had been a working artist for many years. I provided her with watercolors. She said she was not familiar with them, but she was so thrilled and painted intently for two sessions. She told me how much it meant to her and how she was going to paint again.

Another profound experience was working with an 89-year-old woman at the same hospital. She had lost her only son and only granddaughter within the year and her husband before that. She had undergone neck and lower back surgeries and was in severe pain. She drew with watercolor markers on coffee filters and added water to blend the colors. We worked together several times and when she was so bad she couldn't leave her bed, I brought the markers and set up an easel for her to paint in bed. Although terribly weak, she drew and painted for 15–20 minutes until she finished her painting. I was simply a silent witness. Something in her needed to create, needed to express herself. It was *very* moving for me. She rallied for a few months but died within six months of my having first met her. I will never forget her.

What is your worst experience?

I learned during the research portion of my curriculum how unprepared I was to do research. I was curious and willing but without the skills to produce meaningful work. I wish I had undergraduate basic research training prior to beginning the art therapy program. Research is important and I may have been able to contribute something.

Among one of the challenging experiences was having to break a client's confidentiality in order to follow legal and ethical guidelines. It was a situation which felt awkward and uncomfortable, but in the end, helped the client feel protected and allowed her the opportunity to speak up for the first time about her past childhood abuse.

I see a lot of burnout in the faculty and that's discouraging.

Feeling responsibility and weight. Not knowing where to turn when sometimes getting mixed information.

It is difficult when classroom confidentiality is not protected. For example, students sharing your experiences outside of class without your permission.

My worst experiences are the lack of cultural and LGBTQ considerations in the course work of my program. I believe both topics are pivotal to the development of future art therapists and they have been overlooked.

Culturally incompetent and outdated information.

I felt as if the program lacked the academic and professional rigor that I expected. There was little critical discourse occurring and I worried that my education was a shallow and cursory experience. I began to question the art therapy field as a whole.

I got into a disagreement over the internet with a well-known art therapist. She contacted my program in an attempt to shut me up. The experience completely changed my opinion of art therapy being a supportive environment.

One of the worst experiences in my graduate school experience was the first few weeks of my first practicum. I was completely overwhelmed and stressed out by the disorganization of the community based nonprofit agency. There was no designated space for me to work and my supervisor was absent much of the time or unhelpful when I asked for structure. I didn't know how or what to do in art therapy and I was trying to resist my art teacher tendencies. This turned out to be a huge point of learning which was wonderful, too.

I've only been able to take two courses per semester and have been working on the Masters and Doctorate degrees at the same time. Consequently, when I did my first practicum, the class was Practicum II for everyone else. And as an older student as well, I struggled to fit in. I began the semester feeling inferior to the rest of the students and the teacher informed me that although this was my first practicum, I would be treated as if it was my second, just like the other students.

I had asked if I could do my first practicum at a residential program for homeless veterans as I was anxious to work with the veteran population. However, in hindsight, it was not the best placement for my first experience as I didn't have much on-site supervision and worked on Saturdays when there was no other staff present. I was also probably too emotionally volatile for that population: I was introduced by the staff to all the residents as the mother of a Marine killed in Iraq, so personal boundaries were undefined and it was an emotionally charged population for me.

The worse session there was when my teacher came to my internship site to observe me in group therapy. I was nervous beforehand, but when the group began, I just froze up inside. As my teacher pointed out, I only asked *one* question of one client during the hour group. Luckily I was co-leading with my on-site supervisor (MSW, not art therapist) so she did most of the talking. I was terribly embarrassed that I showed such a lack of skill and leadership. It took me a while to get over! I continued to work at that site the rest of the year, but moved into more individual therapy and I learned a lot. I have since greatly improved my sense of self-efficacy, partially through the inspiration from Albert Bandura's writing.

The idea of the "worst experience" is hard to fathom because in the three years of my graduate program, I've come to view pretty much every experience as a chance for growth and information-gathering in my journey.

I suppose the most disheartening experience I have had was at my first-year internship at a state-run medical hospital that had four wings devoted to inpatient psychiatric adult patients. The patients suffered from chronic and severe mental illness (such as dual diagnosis schizoaffective disorder and substance abuse), and many had been incarcerated, homeless, and/or had multiple stays at the hospital. They often spent a few months (or years) getting stabilized, released to step-down programs, stopped taking their medications, and then returned to the hospital. After my first weekly floor rounds meeting with the psychiatrist, social workers, and head nurses, I became incredibly depressed with the feeling of how futile our work as mental health counselors/art therapists seemed to be with this population. At least 90% of the patients, had spent the majority of their lives fighting a mental illness without proper care or support. It felt like it was too late to be of much transformative help for most of the patients and it was apparent in the doctors and nurses comments and body language that they had all but given up on trying to help their patients. The hospital felt more like a holding tank for the patients rather than a place for them to receive support and help to get them back on their feet and grow self-actualization or agency. In the months that followed at my internship there, I found my role as a container and distraction for the patients for an hour at a time for them to find an escape through the art.

Some of my worst experiences have to do with my university and the way it is run! There were many, many frustrating (if not hair-pulling experiences of classes being cancelled or too full for required courses, little to no response to emails regarding questions with financials. Even the field training office was less than helpful when trying to find internships or ask questions about licensure.

Before I started, I received a call from the financial aid office telling me I had won the Dean's Scholarship (one of the only scholarships offered to graduate students). Two months later, I received a letter that said I was NOT one of the winners. When I called to find out what was going on, it was concluded that the man who called to tell me I had won had called me by accident and I had NOT received the scholarship. I talked to the people in charge. They apologized and said they didn't have anything they could offer me to help offset the money that they had promised me. Instead they gave me a $20 gift card to the bookstore. While I am forever grateful for the education and experience I have received, it makes me sad how little financial help is available for folks in our discipline, as well as the lack of structure within the university itself.

The worst thing I've experienced in the last two years is the current breakup I'm going through. It was a serious three-year, live-in relationship, one that I thought would be my last. Although my breakup may appear unrelated to the art therapy program, I would argue that they are very connected. In polling the current graduating class, I estimated about 65% of us experienced a major change in relationship status such as a marriage or a separation, between the time they applied and the time they graduated. Some of that could just be a result of the demographic—most of us being young women between the ages of 20 and 35—but I suspect that a lot more of it has to do with what the program demands of us. We are challenged not just academically, but emotionally and intellectually as well on a daily basis. We are dynamic strong, giving human beings and we rise to the challenge. A colleague of mine described it as a "steep sudden, uphill climb" full of introspection and self-discovery. We undergo a therapeutic process as both client and therapist, and for many students, this is the first time for each. If a significant other is not equally committed or ready for this transformation, problems will arise. In the case of my relationship, I had become very dependent on my boyfriend, failing to notice that the pressure it put on him was too much. I'm only beginning to realize how exhausting it must have been to keep up with me during this journey. He did a fantastic job, reinforcing my belief that he was marriage material, but never actually saying that he wanted that as well. Eventually, we both grew distant, absorbed in our work, and our relationship turned into a facade—each of us going through the motions and initiating the expected small talk at dinner. When it finally ended two months ago, I was devastated, wracked with guilt and startled by his detached attitude during the process. I was sent into "Freeze" mode. Circumstances necessitated three weeks for me to find an apartment and move out, and unfortunately during this time, I was unable to see my therapist. I believe that the last two years—the grad program, my work in personal therapy, and this breakup—have changed me more and taught me more than any other in my life. That being said, I'm entering the next era with a lot of padding stripped away from me: I feel fragile and hypervigilant, aware of my own emotional vulnerability. I'm really just a toddler in this growth process, and I recognize that this process is forever. I'll continue to be molded by clients, supervisors, colleagues, friends, family, and even lovers for a very long time.

As you become an art therapist, who are useful role models for you? And what qualities do they manifest that are important for you?

I am fortunate to have had contact with pioneers in our field, through personal visits, phone calls, and exchanged emails. I feel gratitude for the wisdom each one shared and for their sincere interest in me as a student. As I grow in the art therapy profession, I will remember their contributions to my career path, knowing that I may be one to share my stories with a student someday. I also reached out to faculty within my program who readily shared their knowledge and offered pertinent advice. Faculty members demonstrated how important it is to understand oneself before doing this work and how to practice self-care. This may be the greatest lesson learned.

I feel grateful for the students in my cohort who shared their gifts of insight and understanding with me as we each transformed our lives through the educational process. These may be some of my favorite role models.

Role models are my friends that lead socially conscious lives. They taught me how to think. Thank you!

[Faculty name]who has been both a nurturing and enthusiastic force in my learning process. [Faculty]who took me under her wing and offered me unconditional support. [Faculty] who shared with me her wisdom and depth of knowledge in the field. [Faculty] who shared her contagious enthusiasm for art therapy [Faculty] who inspired me to see the magic in art therapy.

Everyone around me—faculty, students, supervisor, clients and all the other people I come in contact with have all influenced me in some way. Those interactions have influenced my development in art therapy.

My teachers, my personal therapist, and guest speakers. My prominent role model is a teacher whom I identity with the most because of our similar ages, backgrounds, and interests—both being practicing artists active in the visual arts. I also think of my other teachers as strong role models but the generational closeness and similar worldview of this one particular teacher has been very inspiring in shaping my identity and self understanding as a particular type of art therapist.

My teachers and co-interns have been most helpful. I would have loved to have an art therapist supervisor, but haven't had that experience. Two faculty have been particularly helpful: their understanding, feedback and suggestions have helped alot.

I have learned from my classmates in practicum classes, what directives they used, their challenges, and their actions in response to those challenges. I also had the opportunity to work with two fellow students this spring which was wonderful. Seeing their actions, I think, helped me figure out my own way of working with clients. I realized our unique qualities and styles and realized that we all brought ourselves to the practice. I also had wonderful on-site supervisors and staff that helped me feel at ease, helped me understand diagnoses, and supported and validated my role in the facility.

The people I consider role models for me while I've become an art therapist all share similar qualities, whether they are art therapists or yoga teachers. The people I've found most inspiring are those who strive to live as much of an authentic life as possible, and in doing so, bring authenticity, compassion, empathy and passion to their profession. The two women who own and teach at the yoga studio I discovered during my first summer here, not only teach the philosophy of honoring the light within ourselves and others, they demonstrate it by offering free community classes every Friday, participating in local charity events, and serving as a lieutenant at the local fire station.

One professor stood in front of the class each week and wove intricate tales of pain, joy, and healing that he had been privileged to help clients experience in his own work of over 30 years. Listening to him tell of the deep connections that he had made with people along his journey was evident in the tone of his voice and the lines of joy or sorrow on his face as he spoke. [Another Faculty] is also a person I feel exemplifies the authenticity I strive to achieve and understand in my own self and my work with others. Her travels around the world during times of great natural and human-made devastation to help those who are suffering most, sparked a flame inside that brought me to her door to ask if I could be her assistant. The idea of being "in the trenches" with those whose lives may literally be falling apart around them struck a major chord as an example of someone who truly lives her passion.

When I was beginning my search for graduate programs, a wise friend advised me to focus less on the price and convenience and more on the professor-student relationship. If I could find one professor that I really admired, respected, and connected with and make it my goal to work closely with him or her during my studies, then I would get my money's worth. [Faculty name] was the professor for me. She interviewed me to review my portfolio and application, complementing my essay in a way that validated my choice to go really personal with it. Since I've been in the program, I've been inspired by how actively involved she is in so many aspects of the program. Her zeal for the work she's doing is contagious and I'm excited and honored to have her as a mentor. What I didn't realize at first was that I would grow to respect and admire all of the professors in the program, each for a different strength. It is a joy and privilege to be a part of this group of innovative researchers, teachers, and clinicians.

I turned to books and began reading Horney, Ricoeur, Hegal, Heidigger, Merleau-Ponty, Rita Charon, and Foucault among others. I found that philosophers provided a missing element and I attempted to tackle more primary sources so I could discover my theoretical therapeutic orientation.

Fellow students have been a close second as far as mentoring me. Because I'm enrolled part-time, I've been lucky enough to be a part of not one but two different cohorts, plus a small group of fellow part-timers. Each cohort has its own energy and it's been fascinating to note the similarities and differences as we learn together. Perhaps the most important lesson has been the concept of "choosing one's battles." Learning when to speak up, voice my opinion, stand up for my beliefs or myself and when to gracefully defer to another has been a difficult but vital journey and certainly a journey that will continue.

A mentor I have from my last job that I keep in touch with.

People I work with in the community.

There was a teacher at my community college who changed my perspective of art therapy. And in a 3-d design and sculpture class I was inspired to do art therapy in disaster response and internationally. Art teachers have changed the way I look at and do art.

Chapter VI

A MENTOR

According to the Merriam Webster's Dictionary,[1] a mentor is "a trusted counselor or guide." To mentor is "to teach or give advice or guidance to someone." In Greek mythology, Mentor, a friend to Odysseus, was placed in charge of his son Telemachus when Odysseus left for the Trojan wars.[2] In general usage today, the term has come to mean someone who shares wisdom and knowledge with a less experienced colleague. For an art therapy student, a mentor brings knowledge to expand the picture to consider the interpersonal universe and cultural shaping of human life and personality.

(KN) Sometimes students don't realize that support can be attained outside a graduate program through a mentor and sometimes students don't even realize they aren't being supported, or could be supported at a higher level, which compels some of us to enlist willing mentors such as Max.

It is possible I could have developed this kind of mentorship with one of my university instructors, but the demands on instructors, especially the number of students they are teaching and advising, play a large part in the level of attention they can offer. I wonder, though how many experienced art therapists and educators such as Max would be willing to invest the amount of guidance in a student as she has in me? It may come down to the two individuals involved.

I did not realize the level of commitment I had to make to be worthy of mentorship. Much of the time I wanted to wiggle out of feelings of vulnerability and ineptitude that came with having my work scrutinized. I felt this in classroom situations, too, but the focus would eventually shift off of

---

1. http://www.meriam-webster.com. Retrieved June 28, 2014.
2. http://www. wikipedia.org. Retrieved June 28, 2014.

me. In the intensive one-on-one mentorship, not only does the focus remain squarely on me, but before too long my mentor became internalized, and she sat on my shoulder in every client session. When I began sending her write-ups and art from certain art therapy sessions, I felt both fearful and exhilarated knowing that I would be seen and counseled at such a deep level.

(MBJ) This last part is not what I would define as mentoring, which is much less specific about casework. At one point, Kim and I formally evolved into a quasi-supervisory relationship as well as the mentoring one and I believe that is what she is writing about here.

(KN) But the process stretched me and I became increasingly able to hold more and more instruction, and in sessions, I could implement art therapy with more and more courage, skill, and knowledge.

In these times of increased demands on university professors and less resources for students, I propose that an art therapy graduate program assemble a cadre of experienced clinicians from the geographical area around the program who are willing to be mentors. An email address could be attached to names on the list and given to students who might want a mentor. The student desiring a mentor would contact the mentor on the list. The two people would take it from there and work out the necessary details. I *don't* advise developing specific requirements for time, duration, or contact. This relationship should be as fluid as possible and structured to fit the needs of the two people involved.

It seems essential also that art therapy programs continue to assist fledgling art therapists to become established in the field after graduation. A mentor can be helpful here. With so many challenges to establishing art therapy in mental health venues and its relative infancy in the field of psychology, graduate programs ensure their own future when they enable the professional success of their alumni.

I propose that each art therapy educational program offer a free postgraduate group for its graduates. This group would meet on a regular basis throughout the year and would provide support and nurturance, as well as case consultation. I believe a group such as this, particularly in a dual degree program, could provide what is necessary to keep the lonely art therapist practicing art therapy.

As I near graduation, I am looking at my options for supervision; I require a supervisor who has both a mental health license and is a board certified art therapist to sign off on both sets of hours; if I cannot find this in the same person, I will hire two supervisors. I anticipate receiving a handful of hours per month in a group supervision setting to oversee my work.

When I consider how mentorship is different than the supervisory relationship, I see that group supervision and individual guidance are obviously different. My experience working with Maxine one-on-one in what I think of as a professional friendship also functions as an initiation. Especially because of her stature and influence in the field, I feel that I am part of a lineage moving from Helen Landgarten (her mentor) to Maxine to me. This makes art therapy feel like a living energy I am entrusted with. That may be what feels most powerful about the one-on-one mentorship: it is built specifically around the knowledge base of art therapy: concrete and enduring, and yet perhaps vulnerable to dissolution if not tended. The relationship itself is different than with a supervisor, who is legally responsible for my clients. In some ways, the mentorship is more about the mentor. I noticed this in the relationships between Rilke and Kappus, Pipher and her student, and especially in McNiff's fabricated supervisee: the mentor articulates the gift and the student receives it. The new art therapist evolves more quickly through the wisdom of the more experienced guide. Both grow from their different vantage points.

Kim states that she thinks a mentor relationship is more about the mentor. I disagree. While it is assumed that the senior person has things to give to the more junior one, like any relationship, it is complex and nuanced and moves both ways. More than anything, it takes two people who are willing to be open to each other. It *is* a collaboration.

I like the idea of a list where mentor and mentee connect and work out their collaboration. I can imagine them making art together, drinking coffee while pondering a case, feeling into the images made in a session, expanding the presence of the art therapy in the world through the creation of a new practitioner.

Kim Newall came to my house on Whidbey Island, Washington, north of Seattle, as a first year art therapy graduate student at Antioch University–Seattle. She came for a field trip as a member of a class studying art therapy history. Afterwards, she and a few other students made arrangements to come back. Many of these students' regular faculty members were newly minted art therapy graduates and the students longed to talk with someone who had been in the profession for awhile. We spoke in depth about art therapy, my knowledge of it, and their ongoing issues with becoming an art therapist. Generally, we spent about two hours in wide-ranging dialogue, then went to lunch where we talked some more. Our subject matter meandered over the whole universe of becoming and being an art therapist: getting your needs met within an educational program, how to temper expectations and keep moving forward; internships–how to get them and how to make them work for you and your client; how to handle institutional and clinic bureaucracies and politics; how to educate others about what art therapy is. Within what I intended as a supportive, honest environment, we also tackled some of the sensitive issues of treating clients in art therapy and those of how a student learns to be a professional art therapist and not become overwhelmed by the suffering she or he encounters. Eventually, Kim asked me to be her mentor. First, we defined what a mentor is and does and what she wanted.

Our relationship grew from a field trip arranged by Professor Elisabeth Donohue, who recognized the opportunity available to our class to meet and discuss art therapy with Max, a pioneer in the field, and one who happened to live on nearby Whidbey Island. Her willingness to meet with Beth's class created the opportunity for me to begin and continue to share ideas and receive guidance from "one of the greats" in our field. I would encourage other students to seek out a mentoring relationship with an experienced art therapist active in the field to challenge their development and commitment to art therapy. Although, having an art therapy mentor can add a stressor to an already mountainous amount of information coming in, it forces a prioritizing of art therapy in the midst of many competing factors.

It was a long drive and a ferry ride to Whidbey Island from where they lived, and students, of course, are overwhelmingly busy. Eventually, the group became two, Kim and another graduate student. Later it became one–Kim. We continued our process of talking for a few hours and then going to lunch. This arrangement has now been going on for three years and Kim is close to graduation.

What did I charge? Nothing, other than they paid for my lunch. (We usually had hamburgers and fries.) A few years back, I made the decision not to charge a fee for professional training services. I knew students are always poor–if they weren't when they start their educational program, they usually are when they finish and I wanted this mentoring relationship to be free from the strains and ambivalences of payment when you don't have much. I viewed my mentoring as a gift to these students and to the profession. Besides, it gave me pleasure and kept me on my toes as a thinking and feeling art therapist.

Through an oral history-like process, I enjoyed being able to pass on knowledge of the ins and outs of the field as I knew it, hoping that it would live in these students as it has in me. Moreover, I love working with students with their clear eyes, fresh ideas, passion, and sometimes, their downright bumbling. Working with them enables me to keep turning over and reconsidering old questions, but in a fresh way. I learned much from them. An art therapy student needs a mentor. An art therapist mentor needs a mentee.

Today, most art therapy educational programs are "dual degreed." First introduced about 1980, dual-degree programs were originally established as curriculums for state licensing–a necessary and pragmatic move to protect the right of the art therapist student *to work after graduation*–certainly a worthy goal. Unfortunately, this form of education seems to have morphed into one where identity confusion for the art therapy student is increased and ubiquitous.[3] It should be simple: *"An art therapist is someone who does art therapy."* But it is not. Functionally, a dual-degree curriculum attempts to train two kinds of therapists at the same time: One is a talk therapist–often a counselor these days–who doesn't necessarily use art. Hypothetically, a dual-degree program can be an integrated curriculum, but it usually isn't. How could it help but be confusing for the art therapy student and for staff at internship sites who may have little understanding of art therapy and its vicissitudes? When a student begins an internship, she or he may train in a place that has never had an art therapist before and she or he is likely to encounter agency staff that have little, if any, real knowledge of what art therapy is. There may be pallid support for art therapy and sometimes even a belittling of it.

In my graduate program, I toggled between the art therapy department and the counseling program. For my first few quarters, I went along with counseling assignments as they were presented. Then one day I noticed an art therapy student setting up her art supplies in a counseling class and it dawned on me I needed to actively bring the two sides of my academic life together! I was shocked this had not occurred to me before,

3. See Junge, M. (2014). *Identity and art therapy: Personal and professional perspectives.* Springfield, IL: Charles C Thomas.

nor that I had been instructed to do it. Somehow bringing in art often felt risky. Others encouraged it. Counseling colleagues were intrigued and there was even talk of a course for them to take in our department. But cross-pollination seemed to go in one direction only as art therapy students migrated to capture credibility from the Psychology department, yet counseling students weren't allowed to learn basic art therapy skills. I wondered if it was because their acquisition of art therapy knowledge might endanger our own standing as specialists? Eventually, I came to incorporate art therapy into all my classes which usually surprised the counseling students with what was so quickly and creatively revealed through the art. I would suggest dual-degree programs explicitly address the crossing of worlds, since it is a central concern extending from the beginning of the academic experience, to internship and beyond. I would have welcomed instruction in infiltration strategies for art therapy and what to say in elevators and other places to effectively promote art therapy.

I am especially fortunate to be placed at an internship site that is committed to having an art therapy department. I am not creating a program from scratch; someone has gone before me. But I am aware it could slip away at any time and I am entrusted to keep it going. I have to negotiate to keep the designated art therapy room set aside for art therapists–no small thing since space is at a premium. Even as an intern, I find I am called to define art therapy and to offer guidance to counselors who use art with clients without training or awareness of the power of using the creative process to elicit unconscious material. Even as I am defining what art therapy is at my novice developmental stage, I am rooting it ever more deeply into the earth of my agency.

Despite the fact that this internship agency has an art therapy room, it is typical–and may be the case here–that art therapy is known mainly as an *activity therapy* and not in its other forms. With confusing dual-degree educational programs, agency staff often consider that counseling and art therapy are two completely different approaches and that art therapy is only indicated for specific clients. This is confusing to both the novice student and the internship staff. The program, through its internship site coordinator, has an important educational and supportive function with internship sites to ensure that the art therapy student can effectively practice and learn art therapy.

I will soon graduate and will be gathering two sets of hours for licensure and art therapy certification. I view myself as an art therapist with an empowering counseling license that puts me on par with my professional peers and provides a "seat at the table" in the systems that employ me. I am excited and confident I can bring the efficacy of art psychotherapy into the healing context of community mental health. It is already happening.

My agency has art supplies in every office. But much of my mental energy goes into creating art-making systems that are portable and comprehensive enough to have a variety of materials on hand to address the needs of the client. I often move from room to room and must anticipate what materials to carry with me. I created a rolling suitcase filled with supplies, then pared that down to a tray carried on top of pads of paper. In a pinch, I grab markers and paper. I imagine my ideal office with a space to talk, work benches, an area for groups to make art and move their bodies.

Internship asks the art therapist to be a real-world clinician through *doing* art therapy. At the same time, he or she should be learning how to *think* about what they are doing. Currently, reliance on DSM diagnoses is typical, often following Intake or the first interview session. This lessens—sometimes entirely—the student's obligation to make a careful evaluation[4] of the presenting client and a relevant treatment plan separate from what might have been already presented via diagnoses and/or intake. Thus the skill of client *assessment* may not be developed and the student may not be trained to take the time to view her or his client as a full human being and attempt to figure out specifically what might help. Without that level of *learning to think* about what they are doing, burnout or leaving art therapy can be in the future.

Most of what I have learned about assessment has occurred during the time I have spent writing my internship log, in conversations with my mentor, and in art therapy case consult class. I am aware of how much more time I want to reflect on my cases, and how very little supervision I receive as compared to the client contact hours I log in. I have yet to apply any art therapy assessment tools learned in my academic training and I am not sure how to fit this into my clinical work.

The way most clinics receive funding today is through numbers (not quality) of direct service meetings between therapist and client. The clinic needs the student to service a large number of clients and piles them on. The art therapy internship student is likely to be given an overwhelming number of clients in his or her caseload. Often these are clients with extraordinarily difficult and multilayered problems.

---

4. I use the words "evaluation" and "assessment" interchangeably.

Because of demands for service, time for thought and reflection necessary for the student to learn from what they are doing has all but disappeared. While a student ostensibly could manage her or his caseload to have more reflection time, this seldom–if ever–happens because of the pressures of small staff and huge caseloads, along with the student's quite natural inclination to try to do what is asked of her or him. These days, a student learns through handling *many cases,* often leading to varied treatment protocols (e.g., of one time a month, etc.) which may not have anything to do with client need.

Interns do not conduct intakes at my internship site. I receive the intake along with the diagnosis (which I must go along with). After a few sessions, I create a treatment plan based on the options for long-rang goals with related interventions selected from the treatment plan handbook. I list art therapy as one of the interventions.

Oh my, "art therapy as one of the interventions." Kim: as a student in a graduate art therapy program, you know that art therapy is much more than *an intervention.* It is a deep and encompassing philosophy about human beings and creativity, originally derived from psychodynamic psychotherapy and psychoanalysis. To learn it takes considerable time, discipline, and knowledge–not to mention money! A lot of the general public and the professional mental health world wrongly consider art as an "add on"–a modality, a technique to be applied in certain specific instances. The trained art therapist understands the depth and power of his or her profession. But those that use art *as technique,* even artists, are not likely to know this and are apt to get themselves and their clients into trouble because to be effective, therapeutic image making has much more to it than technique. That art therapy can be so widely misunderstood means that it is still a profession for pioneers.

I sound like I am writing about the "olden days," but previously the caseloads of student interns were controlled so that they could have the real-world experience of working with difficult clients, but not have *so many* clients, nor such difficult clients, as to not have the ability at times *to feel successful.* Today, clients may have been at the clinic for years, going from one therapist trainee to another (which is a problem in and of itself) and while one of the priorities of internship training is to temper the student's expectations for client change, teaching them that it generally takes a long time, and sometimes doesn't happen at all, the art therapy intern's expectations shouldn't be stamped out altogether! Students longing for "success" sometimes see client "breakthroughs" where none exist. My recommendation for a model program in which the internship student can learn is the following. Given that internship hours are about 20–25 hours per week:

1. Caseload: Maximum of 10 client hours
2. Supervision–One hour
3. Other in-service training–One-two hours
4. Reflecting and writing about clients: 8 hours
5. Collateral work for clients (phone calls to teachers, doctors, etc.)

Previously, an internship in art therapy consisted of a caseload small enough to allow the student time to reflect, write about, read about, and learn from their experiences. Currently, clinics are overwhelmed with cases and they overwhelm their student interns with cases, so that an internship today tends to be one in which the intern gains experience by treating many clients, but not necessarily learns how to think about them.

During my internship, I have developed in my ability to see a client's image as an art therapist rather than as an artist. I use the MARI[5] system to reflect on the meaning of symbols and colors used by clients and talking directly with clients about their images, seeing and hearing what they emphasize about their work; I've learned to attend to how they make their artwork, paying attention to the process as well as the content to inform my evaluation of our work together. The times I have presented cases to Maxine or to my consult group, I have had the experience of really learning to think about what I am doing. Mentorship is one way–especially after graduation–that I can continue to keep creating the conditions to learn.

It is the long tradition that an internship agency *exploits* interns to treat their clients while the internship *student exploits* the agency and the client for applied training. But the balance has gotten out of whack. Often, too many multiproblemed clients are piled on for a student intern to adequately be able to learn. Learning to be an art therapist takes time, space, thinking, feeling, and even extra reading.

---

5. MARI stands for Mandala Assessment Research Instrument created by Joan Kellogg in 1980. J Kellogg, (1984). *Mandala: Path of beauty.* Belleair, FL: ATMA, Inc.

An additional problem in the dual-degree system is that the question "who is appropriate for art therapy and when should it be used?" becomes too central. Staff members and supervisors, naturally knowing little about art therapy have a tendency to say art should seldom be used. The student wants to please her or his "elders" and assumes they know the best way. But this ambivalence and the need to make a choice about *when* and *if* provide more confusion for the already vulnerable art therapy student.

I found it was difficult and confusing to have the option of not making art in sessions. I also knew that no one at my agency was going to pay attention to whether I did or not. Mentorship and art therapy supervision keep pushing me not to let the creative healing potential slip away.

As I become more experienced, I also accept my leadership role in the session which is expressed in my expectation that all my clients will learn to take risks and foster a willingness to do something that is outside their comfort zone. Seeing art therapy at this level has helped me understand its value as part of the process of change, even beyond the power of the image to reveal the unconscious. I have become convinced of this because I have forced myself to insist on art making even in the midst of a feuding couple or during an angry impasse between mother and daughter. I have learned that bringing the relationship into the room though the process of creating and externalizing illuminates the situation; people see each other in new ways and this can open a space for more compassion and even more change.

In my view, *an art therapist is one who does art therapy in every session.* It is very simple and it needs to be. I consider the question of *whether or not to use art therapy,* a nonquestion and inappropriate for training the art therapy student. *The student art therapist learns the depths and applications of the profession by actually doing art therapy.* And it should be done in every therapy session, thereby eliminating the confusion of when and if. It is often expected that art be used within an art as therapy/activity therapy framework. But it can become more problematic within outpatient art psychotherapy. The student needs the school program and faculty to back his or her internship *as an art therapist* and she or he needs a good supportive supervisor for clinical work to enable the learning of it.

For people who don't know better, art therapy is thought of as an activity therapy (often called "art therapy class") or as an assemblage

of techniques and directives–something which anybody with the proverbial box of crayons could do. If an art therapy student is encouraged to work at this level, these stereotypes are reinforced. Capable art
therapists know it is much more than that: *it is a deep and fruitful integration of creativity, art, human relationship and dynamics, and, importantly,
CHANGE.* Art therapy internship students must be taught how *to think*
about the relationship of the client, the therapist, and the art. The mere
inclusion of art in a proscribed number of sessions does not teach the
student to learn to think about the triadic process in depth.

I am sometimes quoted as saying "art therapy is the best thing
there is." When I say this, I am not simply giving a pep talk. To explain: in my view, it is the most helpful therapy there is, and here's
why: *Because the client-created art image is a concrete product that exists and
lasts over time.* I know of no other therapy that has that advantage (although with the onslaught of new technology, video recording or some
other pictorial method may come to serve an important function).
Words float away and are a second-level abstraction at best, already
distant from immediate experience. But the image created by the
client, even one unsophisticated as an art maker, remains in the mind
and heart and visibly on the paper which the client can come back to
at will and use as a touchstone. I have been surprised by clients who
return to therapy after many years, still remembering their long-ago
images with clarity and freshness. I believe the art therapist has something that no other therapist has, but the student needs careful training
to learn to effectively use the magic of the art in therapy.

**Being an art therapist carries with it the responsibility to educate oth-
ers about the power of art therapy. During a recent experiential workshop
I led at my agency, other interns and staff–many unfamiliar with using the
creative process with clients–were quite surprised at how much of their
inner lives were illuminated by creating an image. One person told me she
created a special professional altar around her creation and it continues to
inform her. To what degree do I teach counselors how to use art therapy?
It seems I should educate others about its *potential* and then ask for refer-
rals!**

Becoming a good art therapist is a complicated process. That it is
also thrilling is what keeps students and "grown up" art therapists at it.
While trials may be many, the pleasures can be extraordinary. But the
student art therapist needs a *team*–a collaboration between the educa-

tional program and the internship to ease the way along the path. It is too difficult to do alone. And, I believe, every student needs a mentor as part of the team.

A mentor can provide a continuing source of support and insistence that the novice art therapist use art-making in the internship healing relationship. This is a time when so many factors can conspire against it: time, space, lack of other art therapists in an agency. There can also be disinterest or even downright dismissal by supervisors or clinic staff and interns due to their ignorance of the value of art therapy. It could be so easy to lose the art in the midst of the pressures of internship when faced with ignorance about what art therapy is.

Clients are often reluctant to engage in art-making, perhaps because they are afraid to try something unfamiliar, have had previous discouragements in their creative expression, and/or fear what may be revealed when the conscious mind's defenses are circumvented. This can be very hard on the vulnerable novice art therapist. Learning to handle this form of resistance may be a student's most important lesson.

My mentoring relationship has provided this source of insistence. At times, it has added increased stress to an already pressure-filled internship and graduate experience and I have been reluctant to add to my already overfull education. However, I realize without this added impetus to grow as an art therapist, I faced the likelihood of letting art making slip away into the default of becoming a counselor rather than an art therapist. I hear many similar concerns from other art therapy interns.

I'm afraid the potential of "letting the art slip away" is a central problem of dual-degree programs, often leading to an unfortunate identity confusion for the student art therapist.

It is definitely true that my growing identity as an art therapist required seeking out a mentorship relationship beyond that offered by my university. I have had to really pressure myself to implement art therapy and being accountable to my mentor has been essential. As my internship unfolds, I am discovering that my commitment to facilitate image making is growing stronger because I have the images of my clients that now live in me; often the images inhabit my imagination in a way that their words can't. I am learning the concreteness and stability of the image, so utterly unique to my client's soul, as a central healing agent we can both see, and watch develop.

A changing sequence of images provides proof of the client's courage to create and commit to change. One client recently drew (with great reluctance, hiding her paper the whole time she was drawing) a magnificent four-petalled flower with a balloon-like center ready to burst. The image created an expectation in us both of something big that wanted to bloom in her life even though her words conveyed the opposite, presenting her as interminably stuck. There was a sudden hope in the room as a result. Now her bulbous flower comes into my mind when I am pressing a client to create something, reminding me there is often something amazing and powerful just out of sight, not yet made. I needed my mentor to press me to develop the art therapist that might otherwise have remained unexpressed. Mentors keep development happening.

What does one need to be a good mentor? I think the senior art therapist/mentor must actively remember *what it was like to be a student*—with all the excitement and passion, vulnerability, ambivalence, self-questioning, fear, and urgency that she or he may have felt then. For the mentor, to work with a student is to keep empathy alive. Without ever having to speak words, the mentor embodies the message that the art therapy student will be able to find the way. Without ever having to speak words, the mentor embodies the message that the process of becoming a career professional art therapist can be survived. The mentor illustrates that when the student graduates and journeys through the years of her or his career as an art therapist, she or he can flourish and even find joy.

Being with a mentor makes my future feel tangible and likely. I see that if I keep working at it, eventually I will become more skilled and effective, less inexperienced and intimidated. Each session is a fresh situation to try out new things, and the results are always new, too. I am continually reminded by teachers, supervisors, and my mentor that it takes a long time to get good at this work, and I breathe deeply in the moments when things seem to go smoothly. For me, increasing confidence allows for more relaxed curiosity and a willingness to take more risks. The ease and certainty that Maxine expresses in her guidance lets me know that I, too, will have those qualities someday.

Chapter VII

LETTERS TO A YOUNG ART THERAPIST

WRITERS

Maxine Borowsky, Junge, Ph.D., LCSW, ATR[1]-BC,[2] HLM[3] is an author of this book.

Sandra Graves-Alcorn, Ph.D., LPAT, ATR-BC was the youngest of the founders of the American Art Therapy Association (AATA) and served on its first board as Chair of Education. She became Chair of AATA's Standards Committee and wrote the first criteria for art therapy Registration, as well as registered the first art therapists. Later, Dr. Graves-Alcorn served as President of AATA. Founding The Institute of Expressive Therapies at the University of Louisville in 1969, she was hired the same day the AATA was chartered on the grounds. With Vija Lusebrink, she coauthored *The Expressive Therapies Continuum,* which became a foundation for the field. She is the author of *Expressions of Healing, Embracing the Process of Grief,* which is now an e-book. After 30 years as a professor, Dr. Graves-Alcorn opened a private practice and owned two counseling agencies as well as a foster care agency. Retired, she now lives in Florida.

Cliff Joseph, B.F.A., ATR-BC was the first African-American member of the American Art Therapy Association (AATA). His interest in art therapy began over 50 years ago during the Civil Rights Movement when he met Edith Kramer at the Abraham Jacobi Hospital in

---

1. "ATR" is "Registered Art Therapist."
2. "B.C." is "Board Certified."
3. HLM" is "Honorary Life Member." It is the highest award given by the American Art Therapy Association.

New York City who invited him to the formation meeting of AATA in 1967 at Hahnemann Medical College. Joseph is a pioneer art therapist known for his struggle for social justice, multiculturalism, social activism, and his role as a systemic agent of change. His work has essentially been in communities of racial and economic oppression and he has been a loud and convincing voice for justice in the art therapy profession. Joseph was Director of Art Therapy at Albert Einstein College of Medical Hospital at Yeshiva University and later at Lincoln Community Mental Health Center. He was instrumental in founding a prison program in "The Tombs" funded by grants from the New York State Commission on the Arts in New York City. Joseph joined Dr. Joe Garai and Dr. Art Robbins at Pratt Institute to design and implement one of the first art therapy programs in the United States; he taught and supervised Pratt art therapy students for many years. He is a much revered and beloved mentor of minority art therapists. In 1973, he organized a panel for AATA, "Art Therapy and the Third World"; this later became a monograph. *Murals of the Mind, Images of a Psychiatric Community,* coauthored and published in 1973. Joseph is well-known as a painter of protest including a series of paintings about racism and against the Vietnam war. He has had many exhibits of his work.

Frances F. Kaplan, D.A., ATR-BC holds a doctorate in art therapy from New York University. She has extensive experience teaching, practicing, publishing, and presenting in the field and is the author of *Art, Science and Art Therapy, and Art Therapy and Social Action.* She is currently at work on a book about art therapy assessments. Dr. Kaplan was the Executive Editor of *Art Therapy, Journal of the American Art Therapy Association.* A past director of the art therapy Master's program at Hofstra University, she has taught at Marylhurst University in Oregon since 1997.

Myra Levick, Ph.D., ATR-BC, HLM established the creative arts therapy program at Hahnemann Hospital and Medical College (now Drexel University) in Philadelphia. Hahnemann was the first graduate program to matriculate and graduate art therapy students. She is one of the founders of the American Art Therapy Association (AATA) and its first President. She was Executive Editor of *The Arts in Psychotherapy: An International Journal* and has published many books and articles. Her books focus on children's art and developmental processes. Some are: *They Could Not Talk and So They Drew: Children's*

Styles of Coping and Thinking and *See What I'm Saying: What Children Tell us Through Their Drawings.* In 2009 Dr. Levick published the *Levick Emotional and Cognitive Art Therapy Assessment: A Normative Study.* The New "Myra Levick Award for Excellence in Art Therapy" given by the community of art therapists is named in her honor. She lives in Florida.

Cathy Malchiodi, Ph.D., LPCC, LPAT, ATR-BC, HLM is the President of Art Therapy Without Borders and Director of the Trauma-Informed Practices and Expressive Arts Therapy Institute. She has written and/or edited 18 books including *The Art Therapy Sourcebook, Handbook of Art Therapy, Art Therapy and Health Care,* and *Understanding Children's Drawings.* Dr. Malchiodi has given over 350 invited keynote addresses, workshops, and courses throughout the United States and internationally. She is an Honorary Life Member of the American Art Therapy Association and received Kennedy Center Honors for her international work in art therapy. She is also a syndicated writer for *Psychology Today* and gave the very first TEDX talk on art therapy in October 3012.

Shaun McNiff, Ph.D. founded the first integrated arts in therapy graduate program at Lesley University in Cambridge, Massachusetts in 1974. He is an exhibiting painter and author whose books include: *Integrating the Arts in Therapy: History, Theory, and Practice; Art as Research; Art Heals; Art as Medicine; Trust the Process: An Artist's Guide to Letting Go; Art-based Research,* and others which have been translated into Chinese, Japanese, Spanish, and Portuguese. A past President of the American Art Therapy Association, McNiff has received various honors and awards including AATA's Honorary Life Member Award. In 2002, Lesley appointed him as its first University Professor.

Bruce L. Moon, Ph.D., ATR-BC, HLM is a Professor of art therapy, and cofounder of the Doctorate of Art Therapy program at Mount Mary University in Milwaukee. He is recipient of the 2009 Honorary Life Member Award from the Buckeye Art Therapy Association and the 2007 Honorary Life Member Award from the American Art Therapy Association; his doctorate is from Union Institute. Dr. Moon is author of seven books including *Existential Art Therapy, Ethical Issues in Art Therapy,* and *The Role of Metaphor in Art Therapy.* He is the editor of *Working with Images: The Art of Art Therapists,* and coeditor of *Word Pictures: The Poetry and Art of Art Therapists.* His clinical practice is focused on the treatment of emotionally disturbed adolescents and his is an active painter, singer-songwriter, and performer.

Catherine Hyland Moon, MA, ATR-BC is Professor in the Art Therapy Department at the School of the Art Institute of Chicago. She is author of *Studio Art Therapy: Cultivating the Artist Identity in the Art Therapist,* and editor of *Materials and Media in Art Therapy: Critical Understandings of Diverse Artistic Vocabularies.* Her current practice is focused on cultivating inclusivity and stigma reduction through community-based art programs for children in Tanzania and Kenya. She has practiced art therapy for over 30 years.

Arthur Robbins, Ed.D., ATR, HLM was Professor of Creative Art Therapy at Pratt Institute in New York City where he was a founder of the program. He is also the founding director for the Institute for Expressive Analysis. He is a licensed psychologist and psychoanalyst as well as a sculptor. His books include: *Creative Art Therapy, The Artist as Therapist,* and *The Psychoaesthetic Experience.* Dr. Robbins' memoir appears in Junge and Wadeson's book *Architects of Art Therapy, Memoirs and Life Stories.*

Judith A. Rubin, Ph.D., ATR-BC, HLM is past President and Honorary Life Member of the American Art Therapy Association. She is Professor Emerita at the Pittsburgh Psychoanalytic Institute and a faculty member at the University of Pittsburgh. She is the author of six books and ten films about art therapy and is President of Expressive Media, Inc. Her books include *Child Art Therapy, An Introduction to Art Therapy,* and *Approaches to Art Therapy.* Some of her films are *Art Therapy Has Many Faces* and *Creative Healing in Mental Health.*

Harriet Wadeson, Ph.D., LCSW, ATR-BC, HLM has directed art therapy programs at the University of Houston, the University of Illinois, and Northwestern University over a period of 40 years. She has published eight books on art therapy and approximately 70 papers and numerous chapters in psychology and art therapy texts. She is a frequently invited national keynote speaker, an international guest lecturer in 14 countries and has led professional delegations to many of them. Dr. Wadeson has received awards for her artwork, her educational contributions, and her research, including a first prize from the Smithsonian Institute for art, a Distinguished Faculty

Award from Northwestern University, the Benjamin Rush Award from the American Psychiatric Association and a Resolution of Commendation from the Illinois Legislature.

LETTERS

SANDRA GRAVES-ALCORN

Dear New Colleague,

My friend Maxine Junge, whom I have known more years than I haven't, asked me to be part of this book and I am honored to do so.

Let me tell you briefly about my own history. When I was in college working on an art degree, one of my classes was on dialectical materialism (still not sure what that means), but it sparked the thought that there might be psychological aspects to the arts. I, like many of my generation, had never heard of art therapy. Long story short, I met someone who did know an art therapist and I contacted her and asked if she would take a student. She would. I studied with her my senior year of college. When I was ready to graduate, my advisors told me I needed to get some education courses along with my fine arts courses so I could do something with my degree. I told them I was going to be an Art Therapist. They argued and lectured—and I did it anyway!

I am telling you this because it encompasses an attitude I would like you to remember: Go after your passion regardless of what others tell you. When someone told me "no," I said I would figure out a way to do "it." The excitement of pioneering into an unknown journey has lasted throughout my life. I do not err on the side of caution, though sometimes that is not so smart, but I have never regretted my decisions. Thus, I started the first master's degree in art therapy[1] anywhere and was hired by the University of Louisville the same day the American Art Therapy Association was founded on the campus there. Why there? Serendipity. (A psychiatrist had spearheaded a program in the late fifties in art therapy and wanted it developed.) The time had come for the University to reopen an art therapy program.

---

1. Sandra Graves-Alcorn: "The University of Louisville had an Art Therapy Masters degree on their books from 1957–1959. The program was an allegedly cooperative venture between psychiatry in the medical school and fine art in arts and sciences. The only problem was that no one was coordinating it. It was the brain child of Dr. Roger White who had become enamored of art therapy. It graduated two people. It's "finale" occurred when Margaret Naumburg was brought in to do grand rounds. She so inflamed everyone that the program was dropped, but remained on the books [of the university]. In 1969 I was hired to reinstitute the program, which already had the accredited sanctions. I totally rewrote the curriculum." (Sandra Graves-Alcorn, personal communication, 2013.)

That story has a theme also: Look for the advantages and the unknown. Be a problem solver, not a "Yes" person. Question your thoughts and others, then look for answers. Those answers will lead to more questions and to many creative ideas!

For example, I was wondering about the commonality or differences among all the arts therapies, when I renamed art therapy "Expressive Therapies" and when I founded The Institute of Expressive Therapies. That was back in the early 1970s and it eventually led to the development of The Expressive Therapies Continuum and Media Dimension Variables, first published in 1978, which are foundations taught in most graduate programs today.

Early on, I was interested in the integration of cognition and unconscious behavior. The more I studied. the more I found linkages in psychiatry, biochemistry, learning, and social behavior. So I am saying to you to look for the underlying knowledge behind the different words often used to describe the same phenomenon. For example, Piaget used the term "schema" and so did the art educator Viktor Lowenfeld, when he described graphic development. I have found that most valuable information follows a developmental model which can assist in therapy or even in the courtroom. Forensic Art Therapy has been one of my passions and giving expert testimony has relied on the differences found in the graphic development of distressed and abused children and the expected norms for graphic expression at different ages.

You are fortunate today that there is so much information on neuroscience and the arts. Read all you can about it. Dr. Dan Siegel is an easy-to-understand writer on the subject. Also go back to the works of Bernie Siegel who integrated psyche and the somatic so brilliantly. Read about psycho immunology and the thoughts of Norman Cousins. I smile when I read all the literature today on Mindfulness. In the fifties, Norman Vincent Peale called this the Power of Positive Thinking!

You are also in an age of challenge with insurance agencies and institutions that rely on third-party payments to do therapy. Even though there are a few states that license art therapists, the insurance carriers have decided not to recognize it as a mental health provider. Gang together in your states and start fighting! I envision a class action that will eventually take place. One of you young, enthusiastic, intrepid new art therapists can be the power behind the new movement forward.

That leads me to one of the questions regarding my thoughts on art therapy being part of counseling degrees. My thoughts on that are ugly and sad. The new graduates have less knowledge in art therapy than ever before. Too much art therapy training has to be forsaken to get the counseling psychology or marriage and family therapy and career counseling courses in. This was done because of the necessity of licensing and the third-party payers, but it has not enhanced the field.

Until you have some experience and a Ph.D., you can't do much about that. But get the education you have missed for yourself during your masters program. Attend Continuing Education courses, the American Art Therapy Association conferences, The Expressive Therapies Summit, even The American Psychological Association. Online webinars are popping out all over. Keep thinking, keep questioning, keep searching, and keep your passion and your compassion. We need you now more than ever. Also, take care of yourself and if you haven't already, develop a great sense of humor!

Best wishes and God Bless,

Sandra

MAXINE BOROWSKY JUNGE

My Dear Friends,

What I wish for you is an exciting and adventurous life, and a fulfilling and well-paying art therapy job. (Or if not "well paying," at least a living wage). Throughout your art therapy career, I hope you will learn and relearn about the wonderful puzzle of human beings and that you will have a constant respect and appreciation for the imagery your clients make and for its importance to them in their life. As a clinician, I hope you will be patient with yourself and not expect too much. And I hope you will learn and keep learning and put your learnings into practice. I want it to be said of you: "She could learn even from a rock."

You are a pioneer in a wonderful but fledgling profession and, as such, you carry an obligation to teach what art therapy is; I know this gets tiring, even stultifying sometimes. Along with being the best art therapy practitioner you can, I believe you have an obligation to do your best to make the profession better and more viable. Along these lines, I'm going to give you some advice:

1. Try to make the world better. Your intentions will not always be understood, nor perceived as positive, but do it anyway.
2. Always try to do your best. But don't expect too much of others or yourself.
3. Between thought and action, there is a huge and precarious divide. Most are content with the former. You be a person of action. While this is particularly important for your profession of art therapy, you can also be an important role model for your clients, some of whom live in a culture of hell and discrimination.
4. Open your mouth and speak what needs to be said. *Be brave–* even when you are shaking and nervous. Speak with facts and with passion. You may be surprised at the support you'll receive from those who are silent and do not have the courage to speak.
5. Be willing to be a leader.
6. Be willing to be wrong.

7. Observe deeply beneath the surface and try to understand the cultural, personal, historical, and unconscious patterns driving your client's behavior.

8. Take it upon yourself to understand the institutions of your profession, its "unconscious" if you will. Delve into your profession's underlying dynamics that drive things below the surface, and try to make things more fair and equitable for all.

9. Don't be afraid to speak your truth even if nobody else sees it or says it. Or be afraid, and do it anyway. I believe there is historical progress possible through the questioning of what seems "true."

10. Question assumptions posing as "truth." There are many of these around.

11. Look out for your need to avoid "confrontation," make people happy, be "appropriate," and "be a good girl." Remember: sometimes it's important to make the right enemies.

12. Revere humor. Use it with your clients and with yourself. Even use it with your profession. That life is so funny can make it bearable when nothing else can.

13. Look for the areas of barrier in current life (and in your profession) and try to tear them down.

14. Much of the prevalent American mental health system is based on social control, not helping. Figure out what you can do about this and do it every chance you get.

15. Love art and the image: how it cuts through to the deeper realms for your client, how it can heal, and how it works for you. Although I don't believe an art therapist must make her own art, I do believe that you must find a way to keep true creativity in the forefront of your life.

16. If art begins to fall away in your work and life, question *yourself* as to what this is about. Be honest with yourself. Words are nowhere near as crucial or persistent as imagery. Make the necessary corrections in the road.

17. And remember these three rules a wise person once wrote:
    a. Don't push rocks up hill.
    b. Find a friend.
    c. Stay alive.

I wish you luck and love and always remember you have the power to make a difference.

Max

CLIFF JOSEPH

Cliff Joseph is 91 years old. He sent some of his writings and suggested I excerpt sections. In a letter, he said:

> *Let the students know that we are all here on Earth together as members of the human family, allied in the task of bringing health to the world. And please share with them my love.*

Sincerely,

Cliff

From "Creative Alliance: The Healing Power of Art Therapy and Social Action"

My work as an art therapist primarily has been in communities of racial and economic oppression. . . . The root of many psychosocial problems that in terms of mainstream psychiatric diagnostics . . . have nothing at all to do with the seminal needs of the patient. Each [art therapist] must not only be well informed regarding the client's stressful history, but admit to, and make use of the lessons learned from working creatively to overcome their own. Being in this privileged position enables [art] therapists to recognize within themselves areas of empathy from which to draw. Works produced in art therapy, then, become essential reference points to build a therapeutic alliance. In the therapist/patient alliance–from their own art–patients begin to see the nature of their problems as an individual, as a group and sometimes engage in social activism . . . efforts to bring about positive community changes can be of tremendous therapeutic benefit.

My personal background has been an invaluable resource in my work with patients from contexts of oppression. Born in Panama, I am Afro-Caribbean. My father and maternal grandfather helped build the Panama Canal. My parents brought me to America at 18 months old, along with my older brothers and sisters. We lived in New York City– in Harlem, where my parents expected to find hope for a better life, life was difficult. . . . For me, art became a way to express my understandings and feelings.

People come to us [art therapists] seeking relief from the pain of interpersonal and environmental conflicts experienced in dysfunctional families, at schools, in places of employment, at faith locations, or in social relationships. They may experience a sense of estrangement and loneliness because of racism, sexism, classism, homophobia, and whatever other form or expression of humanity an alienating society may decide to use as a basis for discrimination. The hidden agendas of racism continue and are exhibited in individual, organizational, and institutional settings, as well as in the mental health system itself. [I believe] interpersonal conflicts are best understood in the larger context in which they are bred and . . . organizing for change requires creativity.

Centuries of Lessons

Centuries of lessons,
    and yet so little learned.
Millennia of ancestral strife,
    and yet no victory earned.
Each generation stumbles on
    through its uncertain night.
Not seeing how to walk the path
    of Revelation's light.
What will it take to teach us now,
    before time grows too late.
Messiahs, prophets, live and die
    to guide us from the fate
Where dark temptation takes us,
    where streams of life don't flow.
Where children's laughter won't be heard,
    where lamps of love don't glow.
Centuries of lessons,
    and yet so little learned.
Millennia of ancestral strife,
    and yet no victory earned.
No end will come to endless war,
    nor will injustice cease,
'til wisened souls obey God's Call,
    to make the promised peace.

FRANCES KAPLAN

Dear Future Art Therapist,

I have been an art therapist since 1976 and have garnered a few opinions about what art therapy is and isn't along the way, which I'd like to share with you. My opinions have not been "sucked out of my thumb" (as a professor of mine said about some ideas that were more intuitive than factual). I could be biased; still, I think my opinions have a certain claim to validity, based as they are on experience, reviews of pertinent research, and logic. So, without more ado, here goes.

It has been said that art therapy is a profession looking for a theory. This is not entirely correct. Art therapy grew out of psychoanalytic theory during the middle part of the last century. Initially, it seemed well on its way to establishing a coherent structure. As times have changed, however, and the validity of psychoanalysis has been disputed, art therapy's psychoanalytic foundation has been crumbling. The resulting shakiness of its structure has left art therapy unstable, shifting this way and that without a common purpose.

It becomes important, then, to say what art therapy is not, to set some parameters for the field, so that a firm foundation can be developed. Once this has been done, well-conducted research (of which we have precious little at the moment) is needed to carry the process forward.

What can be ruled out in relation to art therapy? First, art therapy is neither "magical" nor "mystical," as some seem to believe. It is a process that provides help through imagery promoting self-esteem and self-confidence, offering insight in regard to problems, revealing strengths and weakness, and encouraging creativity in general. It can also assist with goal setting by making concrete what heretofore has been fuzzy. And it can do all of this without recourse to otherworldly interventions.

Second, it is not a panacea. It is a treatment of choice for some—particularly for those whose verbal language is limited—but not necessarily for others. Some people cannot be reached by engaging in picture-making, and others can benefit equally from any number of different therapeutic approaches.

Third, the art of art therapy has only limited ability to distinguish a person's level of cognitive development. There is some correlation between drawing sophistication and level of cognitive developmental, but this applies mainly to the work of preadolescent children and those with specific cognitive deficits. It is unconscionable to label an adult with primitive drawing skills, developmentally delayed without further investigation. There are many who have had little drawing training or experience who are high functioning in every other respect.

Finally, although there is some overlap, art therapy and fine art are not the same. Fine art has universal aims and is not so focused on the personal. It puts a premium on skill and values aesthetic appeal. People who do art therapy may have little skill and little desire to become identified as an artist, yet derive benefit from the treatment process. A colleague of mine tells about a client who is an artist and who confirms this difference. The client reports that the "art" she makes in art therapy is not the same as the ART she produces as a professional artist.

There are many ideas accepted as "truth" floating around in art therapy. Treatments need to be thoroughly investigated through excellent research based in reality. This applies to art therapy which combines psychology with art. There is no other way I know to find out with any certainty what techniques work best (or work at all). Indeed, procedures old and new need to be tested and retested because only cumulative studies can lead us to the truth.

There are those in the art therapy community who have asked, "Where's the *art*?" (conjuring up the TV ad of some years back in which an elderly woman in a burger place loudly asks, "Where's the *beef*?") But I submit to you that the lack of art is not the problem, that we art therapists should be asking, "Where's the *science*?"

My message to you, then, is this: Put more science in art therapy. Encourage research, do research, and keep up with the research in art therapy and related fields. Learn to know the difference between mediocre and good research. Indeed, if future art therapists do not engage in serious research, it is likely that no solid theory of art therapy will ever develop, and our fascinating field may not survive as a separate profession.

I wish you the best in your new career, and I hope you will answer the question "Where's the science?" with the words "It is here, right here!"

Frances F. Kaplan

MYRA LEVICK

Dear Art Therapy Students,

It is a privilege to be included with this group of invited senior art therapists to write this letter. I already consider you a colleague and look to you to strengthen our future as art therapists. I suspect you look to us for pearls of wisdom to help you secure that future. While I am undoubtedly among the most senior of this group and have been here since the beginning of graduate art therapy education and the establishment of the American Art Therapy Association, experience has taught me to be careful what you wish for.

So with that admonition, I share some of the high moments of my career as an art psychotherapist that may inspire you to keep learning and some of my low moments that may help you when you stumble. Along the way, I will try to answer some of the questions from students.

In over forty years as an art therapy practitioner in this unique field of mental health, there have been a number of incredible experiences and images that, for me, have epitomized the power of art. Some I recorded in published articles; others were recorded in discarded notes, but never forgotten. One experience remains forever as the ultimate example that turned vehement resistance into the road to recovery. During my time at Hahnemann Medical College and Hospital, I supervised the staff of our open inpatient unit. A member of this staff, a young male psychiatric aide, who I will refer to as C, often disagreed with whatever I said. I was surprised when, some months later, C called and said he wanted to go into therapy with me. We met and in response to my initial questions, he told me he was leaving his position to go back to college and had a lot of anxiety about this move. He chose me as a therapist, he said, because I was a "bitch and if he could survive therapy with me he could survive anything." The negative transference was so blatant; I agreed to see C once a week. For six months he kept appointments, broke appointments, came to my office without calling, drew many images, but refused to discuss them. The more I tried to set limits and boundaries, the more anxious he became. Then one afternoon he barged into my office unannounced and informed me he was "too resistant" to continue therapy. I calmly suggested that before he left, he draw a picture of what he envisioned as resistance. The image looked like a cave produced in rainbow colors. At the cave opening he put a small figure. We could not tell if the figure was going into the cave or coming out. C was surprised by his image and finally told me the cave was like a womb and he was stuck at the opening. Visibly shaken by what he had drawn, he went on to say he saw therapy as being reborn and he was afraid I would abandon him as his mother had. C stayed in and out of therapy for 6 years, completed college, an MA in fine art, and became an exhibiting artist. He kept in touch for over 10 years and approved the article I wrote which included his case (Levick, 1975). He told me his images taught me more than those of any other patient. I sometimes agreed. His imagery changed the course of C's life and my understanding and approach to working with a borderline personality patient.

Defining C's diagnosis was critical in developing treatment goals, I *stress the importance of diagnosis regardless of your educational philosophy.* Call it diagnosis "evaluation" or "assessment" or whatever, but there can be no adequate treatment plan without it. I am aware that some of my colleagues strongly feel that diagnosing and labeling patients is unacceptable. In fact the term "patient" has become more and more often discarded and replaced with the term client. That is unacceptable to me.

This discipline was founded by art therapists who were treating patients in the field of mental health. If you have not yet read the works of Kwiatkowska, Ulman, Naumburg, Jones, and others who were in the first art therapy journal published by Elinor Ulman, you must. They did not "work with clients," they "treated patients." The same was true of authors published in the one other art therapy journal founded in the 1960s by the late Dr. Ernst Harms, a psychologist and pioneer in the use of art therapy. His journal, *Art Psychotherapy,* later became *The Arts in Psychotherapy* and remains a major publication for our discipline.

An interesting example of how a wrong diagnosis can prolong treatment is the case of a young man in his thirties who presented himself to the Day Hospital for treatment because he "could not get an erection and his girlfriend was angry with him" (Fink & Levick, 1974). To be admitted without the usual referral, he was required to explain his symptoms and his reasons for this voluntary admission at a staff meeting. He did so using vivid details of his problem and describing his distress over his girlfriend's anger. The consensus was that he was "neurotic," a relatively benign diagnosis, and was admitted for what was presumed would be a short stay. However, his intimate disclosures to a group of strangers at the staff meeting did not sit quite right with some of us. In art therapy, he drew a bizarre image of his genitalia in the down position with a big bow wrapped around it. Further behavior led to a more complete evaluation and he was then correctly diagnosed as "paranoid schizophrenic." Treatment goals were accordingly established and he was eventually discharged. There is a funny side to this case: I included it in an article I coauthored with Dr. Paul Fink (reference above) and included that first bizarre image. Dr. Fink and I were then editors of the *Arts in Psychotherapy* and when we saw the proofs we could not help but laugh. Our printer obviously did not believe my male patient (or any male patient?) would draw his genitalia in this down position with a big bow and turned the picture around so the image was in an upright position. So, I not only stress here the importance of making correct diagnosis, but *the importance of clarity in documenting our conclusions based on the images produced by our patients.*

I would be remiss if I did not tell you there were sad failures along the way. I think of a beautiful teenage girl who appeared to be recovering from a severe depression. Her images supported this and she was discharged. Weeks later we learned she had taken her life. We failed her and all our ruminations in staff meetings could not pinpoint how and why. I think of a young man just approaching adulthood who was not well enough to return home for almost a year. My own sense of failure in those early years raised three questions over and over: Had I made the right diagnosis and defined the appropriate treatment goals? And, do we always meet the needs of our patients? Can art always heal? The answer to these questions is no.

I cite one more case that symbolizes an underlying principle inherent in the therapeutic process—a principle that informed my practice and teaching of art therapy throughout my professional career. In the 1960s there were no geriatric wards for mentally ill seniors, no units for disturbed adolescents or children. Our particular 29-bed open unit included teenagers, adults ranging from mid twenties to sixties, and seniors eighty to ninety years plus. I will never forget a lovely lady of 80 some years who was admitted with a diagnosis of depression. There was no evidence of dementia or hardening of the arteries. Alzheimer's disorder had not yet been defined. This lady, whom I refer to as Anna, was given antidepressant medication and I was directed to engage her in group art activities. She came reluctantly a few times and then told me in no uncertain terms she could not draw, did not like art, and was not coming to any more art therapy sessions. I decided to take the time to sit with her have her tell me about herself. Still reluctant to connect with anyone, Anna finally told me she was a widow, had raised a nice family, and had grandchildren she rarely saw. "Everyone was so busy," she said. No one needed her anymore, she complained and she felt totally useless. I began to form an idea: I knew she was Jewish (as I am) and knew the Passover holiday was approaching within the week. I asked if she used to make Passover bagels (a lot of work and a special holiday treat). She became indignant at the question and said "of course, I made bagels for Passover." I asked Anna if she would bake bagels for the staff and patients during the coming holiday week. Her face lit up, I saw a smile for the first time and she nodded her head "yes." My own anxiety bubbled up: Having come up with this seemingly great idea to help Anna, I wondered how I would convince the staff to let me take over the kitchen so she could bake as she had in her past and thereby feel useful again. Well I did convince them all: I shopped, provided pots and cookie sheets and Anna baked and baked. We had bagels for breakfast, lunch, and snacks. I don't think Anna sat from the minute she got up till she went to bed. She gave me orders, talked to everyone, and smiled all day. Our Director, the late Morris J. Goldman, a psychoanalyst, discussed her metamorphous with the staff and his conclusion was she did not belong on a psychiatric ward. Anna's case was referred to the Social Services Department and she was soon discharged and on her way to a place where she would be "needed."

After this funny and poignant little story, I never forgot to listen to the patient and because of, or in spite of the correct diagnosis and treatment plan, be sure I was meeting their needs—not initiating something that met my needs as an art therapist. For Anna, baking bagels and feeding us all was therapy.

Finally, I would like to respond briefly to a few questions from students regarding research and dual degrees. I do agree "the strength of art therapy is the ability to tap into and embrace the nebulousness of it all." But I do not believe we can quantify and/or empirically validate what we do. Working for years on my own research, I have come to realize that art therapists have an incredible advantage: We have images to document what we do and the importance of our patient's images cannot be denied.

Yes, we do need to find new ways to legitimize our field. This is the real world and if we don't keep step with it, we will indeed be subsumed under another discipline. This is already on the way and my views about this have been published over the past 20 years. For the record here, I strongly object to programs that grant a dual degree in counseling and art therapy. A real art therapist is very different from a counselor. Regardless of the current arguments for this, we cannot be both. I struggle with the realization that in over 40 years, the American Art Therapy Association and our leadership have failed to secure licensing in more states across the country. It will be up to you–the art therapists of the future. If you have the passion I have–the never ending awe of the power of the image–you will hang in.

I wish you success and joy in your chosen career.

Myra F. Levick

References

Fink, P., & Levick, M. (1974). Sexual problems revealed through art therapy. *Art Psychotherapy, An International Journal.* New York: Pergamon Press, 3 & 4, 277–292.

Levick, M. (1975). Transference and counter-transference as manifested in graphic productions. *Art Psychotherapy, An International Journal.* New York: Pergamon Press, 2, 203–215.

CATHY MALCHIODI

Dear Colleagues,

Becoming a helping professional has many challenges, but you are likely to face two in particular if you choose art therapy as your career path. One challenge is a result of the trend in art therapy education to hybridize the field of art therapy with the profession of counseling. You may have learned from your professors that these degrees will allow you to become eligible for a license in professional or mental health counseling or marriage and family therapy upon graduation. This is not totally a "bad" thing; having the ability to become licensed in a mental health field does provide some security in the job market. However, the job you obtain as a result of these licensures will not necessarily lead to a job as an art therapist; it is more likely that you will find a job as a counselor, case manager, psychiatric technician, or similar position. Your challenge will be to hold your vision of "art therapist" if your reimbursable credential [license] is in a counseling field. In other words, you may or may not be able to infuse art-based approaches into your daily work and if you can, it may be an ongoing struggle.

You should also be aware that the emergence of the art therapy-counseling degree as a trend has had a tremendous impact on the field and particularly on the development of a well-circumscribed, recognized profession. Essentially, it has derailed the founders' original vision for art therapy and confounded the movement in the U.S. for the establishment of regulations to protect the scope of practice and development of reimbursement for art therapy services. Consider this—in the United Kingdom, "art psychotherapist" is a regulated profession in the national health care system and practitioners complete a clearly defined art therapy degree. In contrast, U.S. graduate programs have morphed into counseling, art therapy counseling, or marriage and family counseling with a specialization in art therapy, or similar titles. This creates a chaotic identity for art therapy and builds barriers to achieving full recognition in regulatory and reimbursement arenas.

The second challenge is one that might be even more daunting for you as you enter the workforce. Despite the thousands of dollars and hours you have spent attaining your education as an art therapist, the use of art in mental health and health care is ubiquitous. You will encounter mental health counselors providing creative arts in counseling; artists, psychiatric nurses, and child life specialists in hospitals drawing with patients at bedside; play therapists offering art as part of play therapy with children and families; activity, recreation and occupational therapists applying art-based directives with clients; professional coaches capitalizing on visual media and the creative process; and expressive arts therapists using art within a multimodal approach to treatment. Only a few of these individuals will have the advanced education in art therapy at the graduate level that you have. They may have personally experienced art's reparative powers, attended workshops, or sought consultation and/or supervision, but most will not have put the time and energy you have put into deepening expertise in art-based intervention.

Many propose that art therapy can overcome the challenge of protecting its stake as a profession and scope of practice through research. In fact, you are probably being told right now that you should conduct art therapy research in order to help the field become more widely recognized. However, while art therapy research that demonstrates efficacy is needed, ironically it does not prove *art therapists are necessarily the best practitioners to provide art therapy.* In other words, while research may support the fact that specific art therapy approaches support wellness and recovery, it does not necessarily claim the need for art therapists to provide art therapy.

I am all for more quality art therapy research and there is no question that it is necessary and valuable. But I see the solution to increasing art therapists' recognition and value in the workforce a little bit differently and it's pretty simple: *write clearly about your profession for the largest audience possible.*

For the past 25 years, I have been writing to clarify just what art therapy is and what art therapists do. I am fortunate to have been mentored (and criticized) by some of the best New York City editors and to have had the opportunity to write for audiences well outside usual art therapy journals and publishers. I was honored to be one of the first ten people to be asked to write for the premiere of *Psychology Today Online* in 2008, allowing me to develop a column that now reaches 2.5 million readers. That is a powerful platform, but it would not have been possible had I not devoted myself to learning how to write with clarity and authority to a nonart therapy audience and stepping outside the notion that art therapists only write for art therapy publications. Taking on this challenge has allowed me to express my passion about art therapy to the general public on a global, social media platform and to elevate the field beyond its limited position as relatively unknown approach. In fact, as a result, *Psychology Today* agreed to list "art therapist" for the first time as a profession alongside psychologist, counselors, social workers, and marriage and family therapists in its therapist directory.

I expect one of you reading this to be the one, as they say in the Tom Wolfe novel *The Right Stuff,* to fly faster and higher than I have. If this profession called Art Therapy is to take hold in a meaningful way, one or more of you must take on this challenge. There is power in the written word, but only if you speak with clarity to a group outside the "choir," work diligently to develop your own voice, and express your passion articulately and authoritatively via far-reaching platforms. And I am excited and hopeful to see who among you has the "write" stuff to take the field of art therapy to the next level.

All the best on your journey,

Cathy Malchiodi

SHAUN McNIFF

Dear Art Therapy Student,

I am dependably inspired and renewed by beginners who set out to serve others through the arts and am fortunate to engage so many of you in different parts of the world. You continuously discover through your own experience how "art heals"–by transforming pain and afflictions into affirmations of life and by circulating creative energy into our bodies, persons, and communities. In the spirit of the request for suggestions that may help inform your practice, here are some ideas that have helped me:

–Keep art at the base of the work. Learn through partnerships with other disciplines and communicate clearly, respectfully, and intelligently with them but never lose the primacy of your own.

–Do not forget what brought you to the work, how your vocation emerged or is emerging, perhaps through your own personal experience with art healing. Do not forget how everything you do throughout your career returns to these sources to flow again and affirm what you offer the world.

–Integrate art and life and make your own art no matter how challenging it is in relation to other demands. Art is the anchor. Living it is the most reliable way of transmitting creative energy and support to others. Should we ask people to do what we do not do ourselves?

–Quality expression is important and furthers healing, but give yourself the freedom to define quality in a way that works for you and others. I look for what is natural, indigenous and authentic to a person. Learn how to relax your grip on the controls and allow the expressive gesture's intrinsic drive for quality to take the lead. Let your thoughts move into response mode.

–Keep a large view of "art" as all forms of creative expression.

–Find colleagues in the field who support and inspire you. One person can be enough, someone who sees you and has your back when you go against the grain and say what people may not want to hear, or who helps you lay back when acting may not achieve your purpose.

–Structure liberates artistic expression but try to introduce it in a way that encourages a person's most innate ways of creating. I am always saying things like–"make a movement and repeat it"; "let the forms emerge from gestures"; "the simpler, the deeper; depth is on the surface unseen."

—Learn how to witness your own expression for what it is (what Buddhists call its *suchness*), while relaxing the dismissive judge and the pessimistic perfectionist. This is the best way to help others do the same.

—Remember that *resistance* to creative expression is normal. We are hard-wired to resist the unknown and being vulnerable, which are necessary parts of deep creating. Accept the resistance, and understand it compassionately rather than try to fix it. This is the most reliable way of putting its energy to use and letting it be a gateway to something new.

—As art therapist Bruce Moon says, learn how to be more comfortable being uncomfortable.

—Never label an artwork. Labeling is a defense against the unknown, a power move made by the insecure; a replacement of the image by formulaic concepts. Learn how to embrace what arts therapist Pat Allen now calls "art as a way of not knowing" and how this is the way to a more complete understanding. Artist Georgia O'Keefe said, when you say those things about my paintings, you are talking about yourself. Proust described his art as an "optical instrument" through which readers read themselves. And my beloved art therapist friend and colleague Helen Landgarten said to me, when people respond to her paintings, "they are looking into their own souls." Learn how to respond more imaginatively to artistic expressions, their communications and energies, and by doing this you will be most effective in helping others do the same.

—Embrace the difficulties you will continuously face and realize that this is where you can learn the most and do your most creative work. Mistakes are a necessary part of the artistic process so take risks when you feel the time is right and create safe places where others can do the same.

—Learn how to open to the pain and wounds of another, witness them, feel them as completely as you can, and then let go when the time comes. This is the hardest thing for most people to do and it is the major reason why many cannot continue.

—Understand that healing in relation to deep and complex difficulties does not come from clever solutions but from acceptance and compassionate presence with your own pain and that of others.

—Create with the shadow. It is the source of the most important change. In art therapy, art is too often the shadow of the profession so put the problem to use and make change.

—Beware of scientism and feeling that you have to always translate artistic expressions and processes into another language which Cervantes said is like showing the backside of a tapestry.

—Watch out for the trendy gimmicks in therapy and research, and be faithful to your most natural and indigenous way of working with art and other people. And try to use language that evokes a sense of what the poet Theodore Roethke called "the nobility of soul" that the art therapists mentioned here and other kindred spirits model so well.

—Keep love of art, people, and the work at the base of everything. In 1986, I wrote "Open, open, open, I can never open enough." When you are most disappointed, respond with love and concern. You will find that it works much better than blame which is a trap that keeps you stuck in the problem. I call it taking the bait. Patience helps too . . . the weather will change.

—If you are able to age in the work, always be a beginner and ponder how everything was present at the start. Maybe maturing simply helps you see it better.

Cordially,

Shaun McNiff

References

Allen, P. (1995). *Art is a way of knowing.* Boston: Shambhala.

McNiff, S. (2004). *Art heals: How creativity cures the soul.* Boston: Shambhala .

McNiff, S. (1986). *Educating the creative arts therapist: A profile of the profession.* Springfield, IL: Charles C Thomas.

Moon, B. (2004). *Art and soul: Reflections on an artistic psychology* (2nd ed.). Springfield, IL: Charles C Thomas.

BRUCE MOON

Dear Unmet Friends and Colleagues,

I've been asked by Maxine Junge to write a letter to you about my hopes, dreams, and fears for our profession. I suppose this means she thinks I have lived long enough, and survived well enough, in art therapy to have something of value to say to you. We shall see.

The first thing I want to tell you is this—I love what I do. I've loved being an art therapist for over 40 years now—head over heels, loved it. It isn't terribly fashionable these days to hold such unabashedly positive feelings about a job, but I do, and I hope you will, too. Please know how glad I am that you have entered this incredible profession. I know the world is a better place because of people like you.

The theoretical and practical roots of our profession are art and psychology. It seems to me that the psychology root has historically garnered the most consideration, but lately more attention has been given to our artist lineage. I find this to be a hopeful development. Over the years, some of my art therapy friends have argued that the profession must emulate the techniques and language of other professions and seek the credentials of those professions. While I am not opposed to art therapists doing whatever it takes to attain professional security, I do resist trends that in my view could weaken our identity as *art* therapists.

As I write this letter in December of 2013, there is a growing debate among art therapy educators regarding whether or not to align our educational standards with those of the counseling profession and its professional organization CACREP. I worry that if we go down that road, future generations of art therapists may have to devote so much time and energy to meeting the demands of counselor education that they will have little left to nurture their art selves. That might weaken our collective professional identity. *Art* is the heart and soul of art therapy.

Still, having said that, I must confess I am not overly concerned about us. I think the main reason is that art therapy is just such a good idea. I have faith that you will face these challenges and eventually figure it out. Making art really does help people. I have seen this healing happen with children, adolescents, adults, and the chronologically gifted. I have watched kids create safe places with cardboard, construction paper, and markers where they are in charge and no one gets hurt. I have seen adolescents paint their anger and hurt and proudly carry their canvases out into the world. I have been in the company of adult clients as they rediscovered inner strengths they had lost somewhere along the road. And I have walked with countless art therapy students who *found their voices* in the midst of research papers, paintings, and practica. Yes, art therapy is a profound, benevolent, and powerfully good idea.

Three of the questions I was asked to address in this letter seem to me to be related.

- Is art therapy research necessary to legitimize the field?
- Are there ways to conduct research that perhaps break away from traditional empiricism but are more in tune with the principles of art therapy?
- In what ways can art therapy students bolster the respectability of the art therapy profession (both during and after graduate school)?

The first question reveals an unspoken presumption that art therapy is not already regarded as a legitimate profession. The second question belies the tyranny and dominance of quantitative research methodologies that have bullied and belittled arts-based inquiry for far too long. And the third question seems to integrate the first two in art therapy's insatiable longing for approval by some outside authoritative entity.

So, here are my answers. (1) No, we don't need art therapy research to *legitimize* the field. We need art therapy research so we can know more, know deeper, and know more fully how art and art therapists can be of help to others. (2) Yes, there are intriguing, provocative, and exciting things happening in arts-based research. Art therapy educational programs would do well to help future art therapists explore the possibilities of art-based inquiry. (By the way, *empiricism* really has to do with observation, pragmatism, and experimentation—which are all characteristics of artistic activity). (3) Respectability is earned through competence, effort, and sustained performance. Don't expect to be handed respect without working for it.

For whatever reason, I think some art therapists have desperately longed for others to validate their work, i.e., other disciplines such as psychiatry or counseling, or state licensure boards, or third-party payers. In my view there has been a tendency to wish for a silver bullet that would at long last prove our value. I'm not sure where the longing and the wish come from, but I think they have at times undermined the profession and at other times given form to a collective shadow of inferiority. I hope you can be comfortable looking in your mirror and loving what you see.

I am clearly in the latter stages of my career and, in hindsight, I see now that nearly everything I have published, and almost every presentation I've given, has been a call to art therapists to embrace the artistic dimensions of our professional identity.

It's almost impossible for me to think about art therapy without also thinking about the American Art Therapy Association (AATA). AATA has been my professional family, my home. Like most families, it's not always perfect. But the Association has been blessed with matriarchs and patriarchs whose stubbornness, passions and deeply held beliefs helped us steer our way through tough times.

When I came into the field in 1973 there were only a few hundred art therapists in the United States. Now there are several thousand. We survived our own infancy, childhood, adolescence, and young adulthood. Sometimes art therapy has taken a wrong turn and followed paths that went nowhere. We have endured pedagogic crises, management crises, fiscal crises, and we have survived the rise of Managed Care. Again, art therapy is just too good of an idea.

OK. I am rambling a bit, so let me close with this. Art therapy has been very, very good to me. The love of my life, Cathy Moon, is an art therapist, and many of my best friends are art therapists. I ask myself, where would I be, who would I be, without them? I hope that your lives will be deeply enriched by the work of being an art therapist. You are welcome here.

Peace,

Bruce L. Moon

CATHERINE HYLAND MOON

Dear Young Art Therapist,

As I write this letter, I'm riding the Metra train home from work. The steady thrum of the train wheels as they meet the tracks provides background music my fellow train riders and I share as we leave our workdays behind. I wonder if the other train riders are leaving behind boredom or dissatisfaction, or carrying with them a feeling of excitement about their work; I wonder if they see their work as fulfillment or as something that drains them, if they feel trapped in their jobs or as if they are developing in their chosen work; I wonder if they are overwhelmed or grateful. Do they carry small satisfactions or unmet yearnings? Are they earning a living wage or beset with worry about how they will pay their bills? Have they spent a day doing what they love, or a day working just to get by?

Most of us who become art therapists have experienced the luxury of choosing our profession and the privilege of having been college educated. I feel fortunate not only to have a job, but also to have one that has continually challenged and inspired me over the years, enabling me to earn a living doing what I love. There are many, many people in the U.S. and around the world who cannot make these same claims. Along with these privileges comes great responsibility: to use my privileged position with care, and to make something meaningful of the opportunities I have been given.

So how about you, young art therapist—what will you make of the opportunities you have been given?

I can't answer this question for you; I can only offer my thoughts and experiences for you to consider. Of the many topics I could write about in relation to making the best of the opportunity to practice as an art therapist, I have decided to write about four "c" words: complaints, critique, citizenship, and consumerism.

Let me begin by discussing "complaints" Complaining is an expression of unhappiness and protest. In our field, complaints seem often to be related to job dissatisfaction and job insecurity: There are not enough jobs, the jobs are too _____ (fill in the blank, e.g., difficult, stressful, overwhelming, etc.), the pay is not enough, the credentials aren't good enough, there is not enough respect for the field, and so on. Of course, there is underlying fear in all this complaining, and it's rooted in basic existential concerns—being able to survive and being able to find meaning in our lives. I find it helpful to acknowledge that fear, and then move on.

The reality is, you have chosen to work in a field that deals with human despair and suffering, and with diverse personal, social, cultural, and political challenges. Did you really think this work was going to be easy? On the other hand, your skills as an artist, therapist, researcher, and creative thinker provide you with the potential to create meaningful change in the world. So go ahead and complain, just to get it out of your system. But then *move on.*

Tell everyone about art therapy, sing its praises, and be willing to explain what it is many, many times over. Find your passion either within or on the fringes of the field. And then make things happen. Don't expect your dream job to fall in your lap, but be willing to advocate and fight and create and educate and search and work and fail and try again to make your professional dreams come true.

The second "c" I'd like to say something about is "critique." Art therapists, being the nice people we are, sometimes equate critiques with complaints. They are not the same. Critiquing is a practice of analyzing and evaluating, of deconstructing something to better understand it, and of raising questions about beliefs and practices that are assumed to be good or true. When, as part of the process of critiquing our profession, we identify and acknowledge systemic flaws, that doesn't make us bad, whiny, or ungrateful. On the contrary, it means we care deeply about our profession, hold it to a high standard, and expect it to continue to evolve and improve. We need more critique in our field. We need to dare to question and challenge each other's work, to hold each other accountable, to set the bar high for ourselves and believe that we can reach it. So please, be grateful for what you have been taught, but also willing to question it. Admire the work of your colleagues, but be willing to critique it as well. Let go of the false ideal of unity within the profession, because what unity usually means is that the voices of the less powerful have been silenced. Don't engage in critique to show how smart you are, but rather engage in critique that is firmly rooted in respect for the tremendous potential of art therapy.

The final two "c" words I'd like to address are "citizenship" and "consumerism" in the art therapy profession, and I'd like to address them as a pair. My plea to you is simple: As much as possible, in your professional identity as an art therapist, try to be more of a citizen than a consumer. By this I mean, try not to orient yourself in relationship to what you can get *from* the profession, but rather toward your social responsibility *to* the profession. For example, when deciding whether you will pay your dues to become a member of the American Art Therapy Association (AATA), do you think about what you will get from your investment or about why your investment in the association is important? AATA is our collective voice in relation to legislative issues and public perception; it is the means by which we organize, prioritize, and educate one another. As a member organization, AATA is not simply an abstract entity; we are AATA. We are the ones responsible for moving our profession forward. Your art therapy citizenship can be expressed in a multitude of ways, including but not limited to financial and labor contributions to professional associations. You can also teach, supervise, engage in policy change and advocacy, create new programs, write, organize, give presentations about your work, curate or participate in art therapy exhibits, educate the public, create new programs, conduct research, advocate for the hiring of art therapists, provide an art therapy perspective on organizational boards, participate in critical think tanks, engage in interdisciplinary scholarship or projects, etc. What will you do to move the field forward?

In summary, critique rather than complain; be more of a citizen than a consumer. Also, I can't help but add a few more sappy but heartfelt bits of advice: Don't be afraid to make mistakes; that's how you will learn the most. Regularly indulge your passion for art and art making. Be strong in your beliefs and true to yourself. But also cultivate uncertainty and vulnerability as paths to new knowledge and awareness. Be generous. Be courageous. Treat yourself, your clients, and your colleagues with respect and dignity. Be grateful for the privileges that enabled you to become an art therapist.

And at the end of each day, as you are walking or riding a train, car, bus, or bike home from work, I hope you experience at least some small sense of satisfaction for what you have made of the opportunities you have been given.

With love and respect,

Cathy

ARTHUR ROBBINS

You arrive at your program with great expectations. Art therapy seems to be the fulfillment of a dream: the combination of psychology and art. The courses are interesting, the supervisors in the program are helpful, and you're developing friendships with the students. But a sneaking, uncomfortable thought keeps on crossing your mind. Upon graduation, if you're lucky, you'll earn between 40 to 50 thousand dollars a year.

You've taken out loans up to your neck, and there doesn't seem to be a way of paying them off until you're old and grey. The [internship/mental health] institutions look like hellholes. The supervisors are all underpaid, bored, and overworked. Not all the placements look so morose, but there are a lot of examples that back up this impression. Is this what you bargained for? Why, you wonder, is there such a disparity between what you're learning at school and the professional world that places art therapists at the bottom of the totem pole?

You put your fear aside and believe it will be different in your case. You'll create your own space and find a challenging expression of art therapy. Graduates, however, tell you a different story. Some find a job; others say that they are underpaid; and most complain about the work conditions: high case loads and an insufferable amount of record keeping.

Perhaps you're a student who truly believes your mission is to work in an institution. You believe that you can bring respect and dignity into your work in spite of all these dire predictions. A fair proportion of you suspect that this dismal projection is true and refuse to settle for so little. Some of your colleagues discover that it pays off to get a Doctorate in Psychology or a Masters in Occupational Therapy. Both professions pay more and receive recognition and status. The sad part about this course of action can result in a loss of one's professional identity as an art therapist. In Psychology you become a scientist, and in Occupational Therapy, an expert in vocational skill.

For the risk takers, I recommend a course of action that is radical and nonconventional: Give up the role of art therapist and define yourself *as a specialist in creative and aesthetic expression.* This definition crosses many professional lines and leaves the field wide open. You are not defined by art, art materials, or a modality. You are governed by possessing the soul of an artist and applying your aesthetic vision to the new gaps that arise in a society that keeps on changing.

You are thinking out of the box and are involved in a nonlinear expression of consciousness. You focus on the body, both your client's and yours, and are tuned to sensory communication. Facial expressions, body stance, the gait of a walk, and the rhythm of talking, create raw material for new and different visions. They are the gateway to the unconscious and the magic of discovering a new synthesis.

If you are no longer confined by artificial forms and institutional roles, then you allow your personal history, background, and current life circumstances to guide you to the place that can become professionally fulfilling. Some art therapists are already using Skype; others combine yoga and art therapy. Why not interior decoration or academic and creative counseling? The combinations are endless and are limited by your own creativity. Allow your history to lead you to the right watering hole; not easy if you're out of practice doing this.

You will need all the support that you can muster. A teacher or coach can be helpful. Peer groups, with and without leaders, are invaluable. You may be able to do it alone, but it is wise to understand the value of support.

If you need a different perspective of yourself, try working in another part of the country or world. Shake up your perceptions of reality and listen to your passion.

I often ask myself why there are so many women in art therapy? Is it because it doesn't offer enough money? Are women naturally more cooperative and community-minded and less able to avail themselves of a positive sense of their own aggression and affirmation? I hope not. There is one axiom that comes to mind: you deserve to have a good life and make reality work for you. The world changes, and art therapists cannot live in a society of twenty years vintage. New needs constantly arise along with new jobs. For those of you who have the courage of your convictions, find ways of defining and redefining yourself to the world. Sounds too difficult and idealistic? Perhaps so. This course of action may not suit everybody's temperament.

A few afterthoughts: develop workshops and presentations, and don't wait for national societies to give you an invitation. Keep on learning and developing a disciplined base of information that will help you wherever you travel. The subject of neuropsychology and one's familiarity with the complexity of brain, mind, and body can prove invaluable in this quest for a professional identity. Finding new and different ways of processing material, can prove very handy regardless of where you work. Knowing all the ins and outs of the computer can serve you well, particularly if you are marketing yourself.

Your enemy can be an entrenched negativism or passivity. Your treasure can be your passion, love of the creative, and the quest to reinvent yourself.

Cordially,

Art Robbins

JUDITH ARON RUBIN
(After 51 years in the field)

Dear Art Therapist,

I realize you are already an art therapy student so advice offered to those who have not yet made the commitment to become art therapists might seem irrelevant at this point in your career. However, upon reflection, I decided to begin with my responses to those considering entering the field.

WHAT I SUGGEST TO ANYONE
THINKING OF ART THERAPY

My advice to anyone who called me about going into the field during the past 51 years was to *be sure it was really right for them.* Here are some of the things I would tell them:

I would ask about their experiences and learning in both art and psychology, urging them to fill in the gaps in either or both (these "prerequisites" are now required by most training programs).

I suggested that they meet with, observe, and if possible, assist a practicing art therapist, in order to get a feel for what can be involved in the work.

If no art therapist was available in their geographic area, I urged them to volunteer to offer art in any setting serving an atypical population, but only if a staff member (preferably one with considerable experience) was willing to consult with them.

I recommended that before investing time, money, and anguish in a graduate training program, they take an introductory course if accessible to get the lay of the land.

WHY IT IS VITAL TO BE REALLY
PASSIONATE ABOUT ART THERAPY

Art therapy is not, and never will be, an easy road to follow for reasons including the following:

(a) Earning a lot of money is practically impossible; the rewards are intangible, though deeply nourishing and meaningful.

(b) Being compensated for your work by insurance companies is difficult unless you become licensed in a field they recognize, like psychology or counseling. If you do acquire a license in another discipline it is vital to maintain your identity as an art therapist. This is easy if you are clear about who you are.

(c) Becoming a competent art therapist takes a long time and is a lifelong process. This means that even after formal training, you are never finished learning.

(d) Because the field is a hybrid, there will always be confusion about its identity among art therapists, other professionals, artists, teachers, and the general public.

(e) You will need to become not only a good practitioner but also *a good salesperson.* In order to convince others of the value of your work, you will need to be able to explain it clearly in language they can comprehend. You will therefore need to learn different languages for different audiences.

(f) In many, if not most, settings, art therapists are not highly regarded, so you will need to have your own internal sense of value about what you do. Confidence is not arrogance; as noted (b), there is always more to be learned and understood.

WHY IT IS THE MOST WONDERFUL WORK IF YOU LOVE IT

Because I accidentally stumbled into art therapy at age 27, after being an artist and art teacher (both of which I enjoyed greatly), and because I ended up having other professional identities thanks to further study (psychologist, psychoanalyst), I believe I am in a reasonable position to comment on the matter of professional identity. While the psychology license was wonderful for obtaining third-party payment for services after going into full-time private practice, and although I belonged to several psychology associations at times, I never felt like a psychologist.

Similarly, psychoanalytic training was terrific as a way of learning about myself and how to be a better therapist with adults as well as children, but while I did think of myself as an analyst when doing analysis with patients of all ages, it was never my primary identity. In fact, as soon as I graduated from the training I found ways to incorporate art making not only into child analysis but also into analysis with adults.

Moreover, although I have taught for many years in a Department of Psychiatry and at a psychoanalytic institute, my identity has remained that of Art Therapist. When I discovered the field, I felt like the ugly duckling who had found the swans as in Hans Christian Andersen's tale, mainly because I loved the work, but also because the other art therapists I met were, for the most part, people I could comfortably relate to. I still feel that way; art therapy has been and remains my professional family.

Doing and teaching and supervising art therapy continues to be challenging, unpredictable, and therefore exciting and—when successful—deeply rewarding. I continue to feel fortunate to have discovered something that suits me so well.

TIPS FOR A SATISFYING CAREER IN ART THERAPY

Reflecting on why being an art therapist has been so gratifying for me, I have tentatively developed some tips for young art therapists, hopefully helpful to you:

(a) "To thine own self be true." Polonius said this to Laertes in Shakespeare's "Hamlet," but it is good advice for anyone. Don't do or say anything that doesn't feel authentic for you, regardless of the pressures brought to bear on you.

(a) Don't be afraid to think for yourself. Regardless of what you are taught by others. Much of this will be applicable in the future, but every person and every situation is different and there are no rulebooks that tell you what to do in art therapy.

(b) Don't be afraid to not know. Although many books and instructors will try to convince you of the significance of certain elements of form, color or content in patient artwork, in my opinion, there are no valid dictionaries of meaning.

(c) The good news is that you and the people you work with can be collaborators in the effort to find meaning in what they create and how they do it. *They* are the experts on themselves, and your job is to facilitate expression and understanding.

(d) Trial and error is the best way to find answers to the questions that inevitably occur in the course of doing art therapy. There are no recipes, and exploring options with an open creative mind is both fun and ultimately effective.

(e) You cannot do miracles in art therapy though wondrous moments happen. You can just do your very best to help each person to make the most of their potential.

(f) Help each individual find their own creative voice and their most comfortable mode of expression, which may very well be in or include another art form.

(g) See the visual arts as part of a larger group of expressive activities that begin with creative play in childhood and include movement, music, drama, writing, etc.

(h) Be open to working collaboratively with others in related clinical, educational, or artistic fields; it is fun, helps you to grow and to offer more to others.

(i) Be respectful of the culture of every person with whom you work, whether as a colleague, student, or client. That means tuning into and being sensitive to the ways in which each person is different from you. This also helps you to grow.

(j) Don't be afraid to make mistakes; it is inevitable. You will never learn or grow or be able to help those who are wary and suspicious if you are too cautious. Failing leads to further learning and offers a good model to those with whom you work.

(k) Admit when you don't know or can't help; being imperfect is part of the human condition and humility is a virtue that is a fine goal, though difficult to achieve.

(l) Be willing to be hated as well as loved; feared as well as sought after. If you are to be effective an art therapist, you must find a way for the patients you treat to express and embrace all of their feelings—and if they can do so safely in relation to you, it will help them immeasurably with those in their lives.

(m) Be accepting of all feelings, behaviors, and creative expressions. This sounds easier than it is, because the human beings with whom you work may well be hard to accept or like and their artwork may seem ugly or unappealing. Liking and loving everyone and every visual product is impossible, but accepting is not.

Being accepted for who they are is more valuable to patients than being admired.

(n) When you feel yourself stuck or at an impasse in your work, seek supervision or further personal therapy (you can never know yourself too well or well enough).

(o) Use your own art as a way to reflect on your work; it is a terrific tool that can be accessed on your own or in communication with others—a supervisor or peer supervision group are two possible ways; no doubt there are others.

(p) If you are feeling tired or "burnt out," be sure to find ways to play and to restore yourself. You cannot help others if you yourself are depleted.

(q) Even though you might love your work (and I hope you will), it is important to have a personal life that includes friends and family. Humans need other humans, and while you may love some of your patients, it's important that you not use them to meet your personal needs (which can easily happen, albeit unwittingly).

(r) It is vital to have creative outlets for yourself in whatever art form(s) appeal to you. These may change over the years, but that's okay. You don't have to be an exhibiting artist to be a good art therapist, but you do need to create in some way.

(s) Find one or more communities at the local as well as the regional and national level to nurture and inspire your own creativity. These might be formal groups or associations or informal networks that develop and change over time.

(t) Bouncing ideas off peers is stimulating and helpful, especially when you're trying to develop your own working style or to solve difficult clinical problems.

(u) Nourish your art appetite by visiting museums (and caves and churches) everywhere. It is quite amazing how beneficial this can be to your inner self and to your work. My favorite artist (though I love many) is Mother Nature.

(v) Present your work to others because it is a way to keep growing, whether you do it in supervision with peers or teachers, in papers, in books, or at conferences. Telling others about what you do requires that you think it through in a different way than when you are simply ruminating in your own mind.

(w) If you find yourself preferring any age group, setting, or format to others, be sure to seek it out. You will do your best work when you are most comfortable. This doesn't mean that it will be easy; rather, that it is compatible with who you are.

(x) If you find yourself preferring any materials or modes of presenting tasks, be aware of those biases and try not to let them interfere with finding and supporting the best possible form of expression for each individual you are trying to help.

(y) Enjoy life as fully as you can in all the ways that you can, because it will help you tolerate the inevitable stresses of working and dealing with people in pain.

I didn't intend to have a whole alphabet of tips and these may in fact be somewhat repetitive, but perhaps they will be helpful to you in your life as an art therapist which I hope will be as rewarding for you as it has been for me since March of 1963 when I first started. Although I have recently vowed to "re-retire," and intend to do so in terms of not spending so much time working on book revisions or films, I have no desire to be less involved in spreading the word about the healing power of art. In fact, since retiring from full-time clinical practice in 1996, I have enjoyed traveling to various parts of the world and promoting the profession, as well as helping people in different lands to achieve a higher level of quality in the training and practice of art therapists.

Good luck to you!

Judy Rubin

HARRIET WADESON

Dear Art Therapy Student,

Think of your training as an adventure. Except for meetings and conferences, you probably never will be around so many art therapists again. So enjoy the camaraderie and the learning you derive from one another, as well as (hopefully) from your teachers and supervisors.

Don't be afraid to challenge your teachers and supervisors. Most of us are stimulated by challenges from students. Remember that when you are at your internship; in many cases, *you* are the art therapy expert–if the facility does not have a professional art therapist supervising you. So, for example, if you are told to run a group for 20 adolescents, tell your supervisor that it's too many, that it won't work and that it will be necessary to break it down into smaller groups. If your superiors interpret patient or client art in a highly speculative manner, ask them for the supporting evidence. They may be projecting their own garbage into the art. And be sure you don't do that either.

Most art therapy students barely have time to eat and sleep, but if you can, find time to make your own art. It can be especially valuable in helping you process your own work. Keeping a journal is a good idea, too, if only to show yourself what you have learned as you look back through it.

Remember that working with clients and patients is easy. It's working with the staff that is difficult. Become politically savvy in working at various institutions, i.e., your university, your internship sites, your jobs. Be aware of the covert hierarchy as well as the overt hierarchy. For example, the director of the project where I worked was having a secret love affair with a lowly research assistant. She had an influential place in the hierarchy, though her professional position was near the bottom.

Perhaps the most important part of the work and the easiest part is your recognition that your clients and patients are just struggling human beings, not so different from yourself. In that way you can understand them and sincerely offer them the support they need. This is why beginners are often better therapists than their superiors: They care about those with whom they work. They're not burnt out yet. So enjoy every moment. If you keep your eyes and ears open, you will never stop learning.

Good luck,

Harriet Wadeson

Chapter VIII

SELECTED BIBLIOGRAPHY[1]

Sandra Graves-Alcorn

Graves-Alcorn, S. (1994). *Expressions of healing; Embracing the process of grief.* Hollywood, CA: Newcastle.

Graves-Alcorn, S. (2012). *Expressions of healing; Embracing the process of grief.* Kindle edition: Amazon.com.

Graves-Alcorn, S., & Green, E. (2013). The expressive arts continuum: History and theory. In E. Green & A. Drewes (Eds.), *Expressive arts and play therapy with children and adolescents.* New York: John Wiley.

Cliff Joseph

Harris, J., & Joseph, C. (1973). *Murals of the mind: Images of a psychiatric community.* New York: International Universities Press.

Joseph, C. (Ed.). (1973). *Art therapy and the third world,* a monograph. Panel discussion presented at the fifth annual convention of the American Art Therapy Association, October, New York City.

Joseph, C. (Spring/summer 1989). Art, politics and the life force. *Forward,* vol. 9, no. 1.

Joseph, C. (1997). Reflections on the inescapable political dimensions of art and life. In Phoebe Farris-Dufrene (Ed.), *Voices of color.* New Jersey: Humanities Press.

---

1. This selected bibliography contains books published by authors of "Letters to a young art therapist" (Chapter VII), as well as a few other basic art therapy books. In certain cases, journal articles are cited. But for more information and "richness," the reader is directed further to journal articles and book chapters by these authors.

Maxine Borowsky Junge

Junge, M. (1994). *A history of art therapy in the United States.* Mundelein, IL: American Art Therapy Association.

Junge, M. (1998). *Creative realities, the search for meanings.* Landham, MD & Oxford, England: University Press of America.

Junge, M. (2006). The unsolved heart. In M. Junge & H. Wadeson (Eds.), *Architects of art therapy, memoirs and life stories.* Springfield, IL: Charles C Thomas.

Junge, M., & Wadeson, H. (Eds.). (2006). *Architects of art therapy, memoirs and life stories.* Springfield, IL: Charles C Thomas.

Junge, M. (2008). *Mourning, memory and life itself, essays by an art therapist.* Springfield, IL: Charles C Thomas.

Junge, M. (2010). *The modern history of art therapy in the United States.* Springfield, IL: Charles C Thomas.

Winkel, M., & Junge, M. (2012). *Graphic facilitation and art therapy, imagery and metaphor in organizational development.* Springfield, IL: Charles C Thomas.

Junge, M. (2014). *Identity and art therapy, personal and professional perspectives.* Springfield, IL: Charles C Thomas.

Frances Kaplan

Kaplan, F. (2003). *Art, science and art therapy: Repainting the picture.* London & Philadelphia: Jessica Kingsley.

Kaplan, F. (2003). Art-based assessments. In C. Malchiodi (Ed.), *Handbook of art therapy.* New York: Guildford Press.

Kaplan, F. (2007). *Art therapy and social action.* London & Philadelphia: Jessica Kingsley.

Myra Levick

Levick, M. (1983). *They could not talk and so they drew: Children's styles of coping and thinking.* Springfield, IL: Charles C Thomas.

Levick, M. (2003). *See what I'm saying: What children tell us through their art* (2nd ed.). Dubuque, IA: Islewest.

Levick, M. (2006). Serendipity and synchronicity. In M. Junge & H. Wadeson, *Architects of art therapy, memoirs and life stories.* Springfield, IL: Charles C Thomas.

Levick, M. (2009). *Levick emotional and cognitive art therapy assessment: A normative study.* Bloomington, IN: AuthorHouse.

Cathy Malchiodi

Malchiodi, C. (1990; 1997). *Breaking the silence: Art therapy with children from violent homes.* New York: Brunner/Mazel.

Malchiodi, C., & Riley, S. (1996). *Supervision and related issues.* Chicago: Magnolia Street.

Malchiodi, C. (1998). *Understanding children's drawings.* New York: Guilford Press.

Malchiodi, C. (1998; 2006). *The art therapy sourcebook.* New York: MacMillan.

Malchiodi, C. (Ed.). (1999). *Medical art therapy with adults.* London & Philadelphia: Jessica Kingsley.

Malchiodi, C. (Ed.). (1999). *Medical art therapy with children.* London & Philadelphia: Jessica Kingsley.

Malchiodi, C. (2000). *Art therapy and computer technology: A virtual studio of possibilities.* London & Philadelphia: Jessica Kingsley.

Malchiodi, C. (2002). *The soul's palette: Drawing on art's transformative powers for health and well-being.* Boston: Shambhala/Random House.

Malchiodi, C. (Ed.). (2005). *Expressive therapies.* New York: Guilford Press.

Malchiodi, C (Ed.) (2008). *Creative interventions with traumatized children.* New York: Guilford Press.

Malchiodi, C. (Ed.). (2012). *Handbook of art therapy* (2nd ed., 1st ed. published 2003). New York: Guilford Press.

Malchiodi, C. (Ed.). (2012). *Art therapy and health care.* New York: Guilford Press.

Malchiodi, C. (Ed.). (2014). *Creative interventions with traumatized children* (2nd ed.). New York: Guilford Press.

Malchiodi, C., & Crenshaw, D. (Eds.). (2014). *Creative arts and play therapy with attachment problems.* New York: Guilford Press.

Steele, W., & Malchiodi, C. (2012). *Trauma-informed practices with children and adolescents.* New York: Taylor & Francis.

Bruce Moon

Moon, B. (2006). *Ethical issues in art therapy.* Springfield, IL: Charles C Thomas.

Moon, B. (2008). *Introduction to art therapy: Faith in the product.* Springfield, IL: Charles C Thomas.

Moon, B. (2009). *Existential art therapy* (3rd ed.). Springfield, IL: Charles C Thomas.

Moon, B. (2010). *Art-based group therapy: Theory and practice.* Springfield, IL: Charles C Thomas.

Moon, B. (2010). *Essentials of art therapy education and practice.* Springfield, IL: Charles C Thomas.

Moon, B. (2012). *The dynamics of art as therapy with adolescents* (2nd ed.). Springfield, IL: Charles C Thomas.

Catherine Hyland Moon

Moon, C. (2001). *Studio art therapy: Cultivating the artist identity in the art therapist.* London & Philadelphia: Jessica Kingsley.

Moon, C. (2001). *Studio art therapy: Cultivating the artist identity in the art therapist.* London & Philadelphia: Jessica Kingsley.

Moon, C. (2010). *Materials and media in art therapy: Critical understandings of diverse artistic vocabularies.* New York: Routledge.

Shaun McNiff

McNiff, S. (1974). *Art therapy at Danvers.* Andover, MA: Addison Gallery of American Art.

McNiff, S. (1981). *The arts and psychotherapy.* Springfield, IL: Charles C Thomas.

McNiff, S. (1986). *Educating the creative arts therapist: A profile of the profession.* Springfield, IL: Charles C Thomas.

McNiff, S. (1988). *Fundamentals of art therapy.* Springfield, IL: Charles C Thomas.

McNiff, S. (1989). *Depth psychology of art.* Springfield, IL: Charles C Thomas.

McNiff, S. (1992). *Art as medicine.* Boston, MA: Shambhala.

McNiff, S. (1995). *Earth angels.* Boston, MA: Shambhala.

McNiff, S. (1998a). *Art-based research.* London & Philadelphia: Jessica Kingsley.

McNiff, S. (1998b). *Trust the process: An artist's guide to letting go.* Boston, MA: Shambhala.

McNiff, S. (2003). *Creating with others, the practice of imagination in life, art and the work place.* Boston, MA: Shambhala.

McNiff, S. (2004). *Art heals: How creativity cures the soul.* Boston, MA: Shambhala.

McNiff, S. (2006). Creating a life with art therapy, a different way of practice. In M. Junge & H. Wadeson (Eds.), *Architects of art therapy, memoirs and life stories.* Springfield, IL: Charles C Thomas.

McNiff, S. (2009). *Integrating the arts in therapy: History, theory and practice.* Springfield, IL: Charles C Thomas.

McNiff, S. (Ed.). (2013). *Art as research: Opportunities and challenges.* Bristol, UK: Intellect Books and Chicago: University of Chicago Press.

McNiff, S. (2015). *Imagination in action: Secrets for unleashing creative expression.* Boston, MA: Shambhala.

Arthur Robbins

Robbins A., & Sibley, L. (1976). *Creative art therapy.* New York: Brunner Mazel.

Robbins, A. (1980). *Expressive therapy: A creative arts approach to depth-oriented treatment.* New York: Human Sciences Press.

Robbins, A. (1987). *The artist as therapist.* New York: Human Sciences Press.

Robbins, A. (1989). *The psychoaesthetic experience.* New York: Human Sciences Press.

Robbins, A. (1994). *A multi-modal approach to art therapy.* London & Philadelphia: Jessica Kingsley.

Robbins, A. (Ed.). (1998). *Therapeutic presence: Bridging expression and form.* London & Philadelphia: Jessica Kingsley.

Robbins, A. (2000). *Between therapists: The process of transference/countertransference.* London & Philadelphia: Jessica Kingsley.

Robbins, A. (2006). Moving in and out of the sandbox. In M. Junge & H. Wadeson (Eds.), *Architects of art therapy, memoirs and life stories.* Springfield, IL: Charles C Thomas.

Judith Rubin

Rubin, J. (2001). *Approaches to art therapy, theory and technique* (2nd ed.). New York: Brunner/Routledge.

Rubin, J. (2005a). *Artful therapy.* New York: John Wiley.

Rubin, J. (2005b). *Child art therapy: Third anniversary edition.* New York: John Wiley.

Rubin, J. (2006). An ugly duckling finds the swans or how I fell in love with art therapy. In M. Junge & H. Wadeson (Eds.), *Architects of art therapy, memoirs and life stories.* Springfield, IL: Charles C Thomas.

Rubin, J. (2008a). *Art therapy has many faces* [DVD]. Pittsburgh, PA: Expressive Media, Inc.

Rubin, J. (2008b). *Art therapy with older adults* [DVD]. Pittsburgh, PA: Expressive Media, Inc.

Rubin, J. (2008c). *The arts as therapy with children* [DVD]. Pittsburgh, PA: Expressive Media, Inc.

Rubin, J. (2010a). *Introduction to art therapy* (2nd ed.). New York: Routledge.

Rubin, J. A. (2010b). *Breakthrough: Art, analysis & the liberation of the creative spirit* [DVD]. Pittsburgh, PA: Expressive Media, Inc.

Rubin, J. A., & Irwin, E. C. (2010). *Creative healing in mental health: Art &* *drama in assessment & therapy* [Film and Study Guide]. Pittsburgh, PA: Expressive Media, Inc.

Rubin, J. (2011). *The art of art therapy* (2nd ed.). New York: Routledge.

Rubin, J. A. (2011). *Art therapy: A universal language for healing* [DVD]. Pittsburgh, PA: Expressive Media, Inc.

Harriet Wadeson

Wadeson, H. (1980). *Art psychotherapy* (2nd ed.). New York: John Wiley, 2010.

Wadeson, H. (1987). *The dynamics of art psychotherapy.* New York: John Wiley.

Wadeson, H. (1992). *A guide to art therapy research.* Mundelein, IL: American Art Therapy Association.

Wadeson, H. (2000). *Art therapy practices: Innovative approaches with diverse populations.* New York: John Wiley.

Wadeson, H. (2006). A multi-colored life. In M. Junge & H. Wadeson (Eds.), *Architects of art therapy, memoirs and life stories.* Springfield, IL: Charles C Thomas.

Wadeson, H. (2011). *Journaling cancer in words and images, caught in the clutch of the crab.* Springfield, IL: Charles C Thomas.

Wadeson, H., Durkin, J., & Perach, D. (Eds.). (1989). *Advances in art therapy* (2nd ed.). New York: John Wiley.

Other Basic Art Therapy Literature

Ault, R. (1977). Are you an artist or a therapist?–A professional dilemma of art therapists. In R. Shoemaker & Gonick-Barris, J. (Eds.), *Creativity and the art therapists' identity. Proceedings of the seventh annual conference of the American Art Therapy Association.* Baltimore, MD.

Ault, R. (1986). Draw on new lines of communication. Costa Mesa, CA: *Personnel Journal,* September.

Ault, R. (1989). Art therapy with the unidentified patient. In H. Wadeson, J. Durkin, & D. Perach (Eds.), *Advances in art therapy* (2nd ed.). New York: John Wiley.

Ault, R. (2006). The art therapy lifeline or how was your practice? "It had its ups and downs," said the elevator man. In M. Junge & H. Wadeson (Eds.), *Architects of art therapy, memoirs and life stories.* Springfield, IL: Charles C Thomas.

Betensky, M. (1973). *Self discovery through self expression.* Springfield, IL: Charles C Thomas.

Hinz, L. (2009). *Expressive therapies continuum, a framework for using art in therapy.* New York: Routledge, Taylor & Francis Group.

Jones, D. (1946). *PRN in a mental hospital.* Washington, DC.: Civilian Public Service Unit.

Jones, D. (1962). Art and the troubled mind. *Menninger Quarterly, 16,* 12–19.

Jones, D. (1983). An art therapist's personal record. *Art therapy: Journal of the American Art Therapy Association, 1,* 22–25.

Jones, D., & Jones, K. (2014). Why art therapists must make art, selections and adaptations from the unpublished papers of Don Jones. In M. Junge (Ed.), *Identity and art therapy, personal and professional perspectives.* Springfield, IL: Charles C Thomas.

Kramer, E. (1971). *Art as therapy with children.* New York: Schocken Books; reprinted in 1993, Chicago, IL by Magnolia Street Press.

Kramer, E. (1979). *Childhood and art therapy.* New York: Schocken Books; reprinted in 1998, Chicago, IL by Magnolia Street Press.

Kramer, E. (2000). *Art as therapy: Collected papers.* (Ed. by L.A. Gerity.) London & Philadelphia: Jessica Kingsley.

Kwiatkowska, H. (1978). *Family therapy and evaluation through art.* Springfield, IL: Charles C Thomas.

Landgarten, H. (1981). *Clinical art therapy: A comprehensive guide.* New York: Brunner Mazel.

Landgarten, H. (1987). *Family art therapy, a clinical guide and casebook.* New York: Routledge.

Landgarten, H. (1993). *Magazine photo collage, a multicultural assessment and treatment technique.* New York: Brunner Mazel.

Naumburg, M. (1947). *An introduction to art therapy: Studies of the "free" art expression of behavior problem children as a means of diagnosis and therapy.* [Reprinted and renamed in 1973 by Teachers' College Press–New York.]

Naumburg, M. (1966). *Dynamically oriented art therapy: Its principles and practice.* New York: Grune & Stratton. [Reprinted in 1987, Chicago, IL: Magnolia Street Press.]

Rhyne, J. (1973). *The Gestalt art experience.* Monterey, CA: Brooks/Cole. [Reprinted in 1984, Chicago, IL: Magnolia Street Press.]

ABOUT THE AUTHORS

Maxine Borowsky Junge, Ph.D, LCSW, ATR-BC, HLM was a student at Overland Avenue Elementary School, Palms Junior High School and Hamilton High School, all in Los Angeles. She earned a B.A. with Honors from Scripps College (Art and Humanities), a Master of Social Work from USC and a Ph.D. from the Fielding Graduate University in Human and Organizational Systems. She attended art schools since age 12 in Los Angeles, Philadelphia, London, and Mexico and studied at UCLA in the graduate program in painting. She apprenticed as a clinical art therapist to Helen Landgarten, began teaching art therapy in 1974 at Immaculate Heart College and was a faculty member and chair of the art therapy department at Loyola Marymount University until 2001. Dr. Junge also taught at Goddard College and Antioch University-Seattle. She is active as an artist, most recently doing a series of drawings about mass murderers, for which she won "Best of Show" at a local exhibit. She published seven books before this one and lives on Whidbey Island, Washington (Mbjunge@whidbey.net).

Kim Newall, MA, provides the student voice in this book. She is a recent graduate in art therapy and mental health counseling at Antioch University, Seattle. She earned her BFA at the University of Washington and continues to teach as an artist-in-residence in the public schools across Washington State. Her paintings, sculpture, and prints have been exhibited throughout the Northwest (kim@kimnewall.com).

CHARLES C THOMAS • PUBLISHER, LTD.

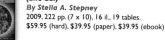